6/18/98

With best wishes

Peter Scott

CRACKING UP

CRACKING UP

Nice Day for a Brain Hemorrhage

PETER SWET

Hazelden
Center City, Minnesota 55012-0176

©1998 by Peter Swet
All rights reserved. Published 1998
Printed in the United States of America
No portion of this publication may be
reproduced in any manner without the
written permission of the publisher
The chapter "Nice Day for a Brain Hemorrhage"
was originally published in a slightly different form
in *Men's Health,* March 1997

03 02 01 00 99 98 8 7 6 5 4 3 2 1

Library of Congress Cataloging-in-Publication Data

Swet, Peter, 1942–
Cracking up : nice day for a brain hemorrhage / Peter Swet. — 1st ed.
p. cm.
ISBN: 0-56838-194-8
1. Swet, Peter, 1942—Health. 2. Brain—Hemorrhage—Patients—
United States—Biography. 3. Brain—Hemorrhage—Patients—
Rehabilitation. I. Title.
RC 394.H37S93 1998
362.1′9681—dc21
[B] 97-48977
CIP

Book design by Will H. Powers
Typesetting by Stanton Publication Services, Inc.
Cover design by David Spohn

EDITOR'S NOTE

Hazelden offers a variety of information on chemical dependency and related areas. Our publications do not necessarily represent Hazelden's programs, nor do they officially speak for any Twelve Step organization.

This is a true story. Some names and details have been changed for privacy reasons.

NOTE TO THE READER

During the Roman Catholic Mass, there is a moment in which the congregation members turn to offer each other the peace of the Lord. This is what I wish every reader of this book, especially those who have suffered the extraordinary mental chaos of brain injury.

P S

DEDICATION

People sometimes comment warmly about what they see as my long, hard road to recovery.

Yet throughout that struggle, I had not a worry about earning a living, or paying the mortgage, or selling the house, or putting food on the table, or otherwise caring for two rapidly maturing, college-bound teens. Only one person could have handled such an overcrowded plate, while still finding the time to maintain her own demanding interior design business. This was the woman I so vividly recall at my bedside insisting that my job was not to worry; my only job was to get well. She would handle everything else. It was a promise that proved far more difficult to keep than the following pages could possibly describe.

Yet the promise was kept. It was, after all, Mary Michael, my life's companion and wife, who had made it.

My television agent, Jonathan Russo, registered surprise recently on learning that Mary Michael and I were still together. Few people, I realized at that moment, would dream of such commitment and dedication to another in today's money-mad, me-first America.

It is fitting, therefore, that I dedicate this book, this career, this life, to the woman who was, and is, always there for my family and for me: to my Mary Michael.

In many ways this is her story, not mine.

Christmas 1996

CONTENTS

FOREWORD

The first time I visited Peter Swet at his Westhampton home, he was sitting at an umbrella table by his swimming pool, talking business with his literary agent. Peter was tanned and appeared to be a happy, successful man in a difficult vocation, an exceptionally gifted writer exceptionally rewarded. He was a lucky man, married to a wonderful woman and the father of two bright, attractive children. He had the world on a string, and then it all went bad.

Of the writers of my generation, those of us who came of age during the last horrors of the Vietnam War, during the period of American life when received values and established institutions were under attack, thought ourselves bold, special, immune to defeat. Yet many became lost to drugs and despair, self-destruction and weariness. Of all of us, Peter Swet was one of the few who not only survived but flourished. From the early seventies, when he made his name as a playwright, through the eighties, when he achieved prominence as a television writer,

Peter's talent, humor, and will saw him through. I envied Peter more than a little. He not only had it all, but what he had was earned honestly through wit and hard work.

And then, on March 25, 1992, in a moment, in the blink of an eye, it was taken away. His brain exploded in hemorrhage, and his life was reduced to endless healing and making do.

What happened to him is absurd. There is no accounting for it, and no lesson to be learned. But what there is, which Peter tells so beautifully in this book, is the story of a man betrayed by his own body, who faces the worst we can imagine, and wins.

Of all the things we dread in life, few fears are greater than that of losing our minds, having the very organ that houses personality and perception, joy and love, that embodies who we are, be assaulted and damaged. When this happens to people we know, even friends or loved ones, they are taken away to be cared for out of sight, put in hospitals, and shut away. What happens to them, what they endure after the damage, remains a mystery. It is in that mystery that much of our dread lies.

Peter Swet has cleared away that mystery, opening up what was secret and closed. After reading *Cracking Up,* one doesn't fear as much; one understands more.

Peter takes us through his life, his working-class childhood, his early literary achievement, his marriage, his successful career, and his drifting away from God. We identify with that. It is familiar. Then, beginning on the day his brain nearly died, Peter brings us into a world that is new and foreign and frightening, yet also brings a renewed appreciation for life and newfound faith. What makes his story so moving and understandable, and finally so heartbreakingly human, is Peter's voice: personal, eloquent, true.

One day Peter Swet entered a world gone mad. The wall between reality and dream had disappeared. His task, if he were to survive and become whole again, was to battle his way back to reason. How he did this, how he found healing, is the great story of this book. It is compelling and, like its author, it is brave.

DOTSON RADER
New York, December 1997

Once or twice a year if you're very lucky you get to pick up a book you can't put down, or at least don't want to put down because it has drawn you into its world so compellingly, so insistently that it becomes your world, your journey, your roller-coaster ride. Just as you haven't seen anyone jumping off a roller-coaster at the top of the loop, you can't jump off this irresistible roller-coaster of a book.

To be totally honest—and this book sets you off in that direction like the running brakeman in a downhill bobsled race—I wasn't exactly looking forward to reading this book. *Cracking Up*? A book about a friend's massive stroke? A traumatic brain injury? The agony of mental and physical dislocation of the senses? Can't communicate with yourself, much less anyone else? Losing your wits, your house, your job, your family, and very nearly, your life? Doesn't sound exactly like a bundle of laughs, does it?

And to add new pains to old ones, I feared, what made even more daunting the task of reading this manuscript on the play-by-play and misplay account of a friend's massive brain hemorrhage was the feeling that I already felt surrounded by this outrageous insult to our intelligence. Years ago I had seen the humiliating effects of a stroke on my brilliant sixty-five-year-old father. At this moment, I am calling brother-in-law and lifetime friend Ben O'Sullivan to hear the downs and ups of his massive stroke. And only last week my friend Yaedi Ignatow lost her father, the distinguished poet David Ignatow, to a yearlong struggle with this invisible terror.

So, turning to *Cracking Up,* I thought, Oh Lord, after talking with my sister Sonya every day about Ben's crack-up, aware of Yaedi's postmortem demands, is my little tank of empathy drained to empty?

Not to worry, readers, not to worry. In his preface, author Peter Swet promises that his book will be different. Promises, promises, you're thinking. Well, having just put the book down, reluctantly, I hasten to tell you that patient Peter Swet (and both definitions apply) has made good on his promise not with a vengeance but with the gift of laughter, insight, a writing talent that jumps off the page, and finally, the gift of love, that very strange and elusive human emotion all the geniuses of literature keep trying to define. What you're about to hear is a big mouthful—try not to dismiss it as the prototypical hyperbole of a blurb writer—but when you finish this terrifying and frequently hilarious and finally mind-blowing inspirational book, you may agree with me that Peter Swet's personal case history on the explosion of an excellent brain makes Norman Vincent Peal's *Power of Positive Thinking* sound like a book on the Nattering Nabobs of Negativity. The first thing that catches you about *Cracking Up* is that it cracks you up. I mean, literally. The subtitle begins to give you the idea: "Nice Day for a Brain Hemorrhage."

When I first met Peter Swet, as a fellow Westhampton writer, he was a delightful companion, successfully writing excellent interviews with world-class celebrities for the mass-circulation magazine *Parade.* Living in a lovely house on a secluded woody lane with lovely kids getting through high school, a lovely, ruthful life force of a wife, Mary Michael, and lively band of friends, including writers Dotson Rader and Mike Miller, with whom he was busily occupied writing a new play. Peter was the congenial creator and captain of the informal local writing group that gathered to drink and complain about the dumb editors, the dumb agents, and even sometimes the dumb readers who just don't seem to appreciate us. The bitching was fun, of course, and Peter brought a lot of wit and high spirit to the game. But he also brought innovative ideas for setting up activities and events that would give purpose to the Westhamptom writers and give something back to the community we really loved, the 2,000 of our village, before the 20,000 vandals stage their annual summer invasion.

And then, WHAM!—the bursting of a blood vessel, which the die-hard writer buried in the suddenly stricken Peter relates to that moment in *A Night to Remember* when the boilers and generators of the *Titanic* explode one by one and the great ship goes down, with the ship's orchestra on deck playing "Nearer My God to Thee." Only Peter is hearing it more like Gloria Gaynor's hit of the seventies, "I Will Survive."

Survival Step Number One is to somehow reach out with broken brain and discombobulated body to friend and neighbor Bertel Bruun, a leading neurologist, the jovial Dane of our little club without rules, who manages to get Peter helicopting to the imminent brain surgery that will save his life, but first send him bowling into his long day's journey into night.

But from somewhere in that deep black hole we knew so recently as bright Peter Swet, came a faint echo of "I Will Survive."

And survive he does, survive what he calls "The Loony Bin," with a cast of "loonies" that are up there with the Marx Brothers and the Three Stooges, and that's not looking down on the unfortunate for cheap-shot laughs, because that's the way Peter sees them. He sees them funny. He sees himself funny. He goes down a hall in the hospital and doesn't know left from right or up from down and can't find his way back unless his door is clearly marked, *Peter's Room.* And all his fellow patients' rooms are stamped with their names as well. It's as if he's fallen down the rabbit hole into Peter's Asunderland, where nothing makes sense, and yet some ridiculous logic is at work, an adventure the author somehow manages to reconstruct: terror in the form of slapstick comedy.

Behind the power of laughter as an anesthetic for the physical pain of stretching atrophied muscles and a jumbled brain, what begins to creep through and grow in the engrossing story is the power of hope—the very act of writing this book, a seemingly futile, even absurdist effort in the beginning, becomes an act of healing. Through this at first imperceptible, then more intense healing, the book begins to take shape. Peter Swet, the writer who suddenly had lost the power even to hold a pen in his hand, much less hold a coherent thought in his head, minute by minute, day by day, year by year, becomes a writer again. Becomes Peter Swet again. Becomes the husband yearning to return to his loving Mary Michael again. The lapsed Catholic self-confessed atheist becomes a believer again, in an epiphany all the more convincing for its refusal to convert. No proselytizing here, no preaching, no sentimental "Nearer My God to Thee." Sing no sad song for me, Peter is telling us.

Awe is an emotion we feel when we confront something bigger than ourselves. Better than ourselves. The total absence of self-pity as he does battle with chaos, madness, terror, helplessness, and the black holes of despair—and with the help of loved ones returns to the world a deeper, spiritually stronger Peter Swet—is awesome. Let's take back the kids' favorite word and use it as it was originally intended.

In anybody's language, Peter Swet has come back from his "loony bin" with an awesome book. I'm tempted to call it the *Rocky* of brain-damage literature. Only, Sylvester Stallone was faking his punches. In Peter Swet you get the real thing. And with "my Mary Michael" as his leading lady in the best sense of the word, comes a love story that lets the sun shine in to all the dark places.

In a battle of the spirit, a battle of the will, in the name of love, Peter Swet has made his Long Day's Journey into Light.

BUDD SCHULBERG
Brookside, Quogue, NY
December 24, 1997

PREFACE

"All poets are mad."
ROBERT BURTON

"One of my few real remaining problems, which is why it is taking forever to write this damned book," I wrote in an early draft, "is that my organizational skills remain a bit muddled."

A bit? I was a mess! When I'd finished dusting the paintings at home, for example, the living room resembled the Krazy Korner at Rye Beach Playland. And when I set the dining table one evening, my wife joked that it looked ready for the Mad Hatter's Tea Party.

I knew I was confused and disorganized.

It was this knowledge that raised hair follicles and caused a clammy ooze in my palms whenever I thought about beginning a book that would rely on my personal journal: a journal that I had, in fact, lost at that point and that no amount of house searching could locate. I finally found it in an attic box marked "kitchen supplies."

Such disorganization gives some idea of why it took me, a fairly accomplished and speedy writer, more than four years to finish what you have now begun to read. In that time,

MORE THAN 2,500,000 PEOPLE

have been hospitalized with brain damage in the United States alone.

Most brain injuries are the result of car, motorcycle, or biking accidents; of household falls; of muggings and beatings; of artery-popping drugs; or, as in my own case, of a cerebral blood vessel that hemorrhaged due to an unknown cause. The medical name for this occurrence is hemorrhagic stroke.

A fourteen-year-old boy in my daughter's school died of a burst brain aneurysm, a similar situation, a month or so before my own experience. Just about our entire little village of Westhampton Beach, Long Island, came out for the poor kid's funeral. I was forty-nine and became brain damaged, yet I survived.

No one can say why a teenager should die and a middle-aged man who has had a full life should survive, yet here I am.

Thanks to a long list of American comedic images from Daffy Duck to the Three Stooges, there remains a popular notion that when a person blacks out from a severe blow to the head, one need simply toss a glass of water at the face to chase away the "birdies," then all will be fine. The reality is that this person, if he or she survives, may be forced to endure months of hospitalization with additional years of daily therapy.

Brain injury sometimes causes profound changes in one's emotional, psychological, or spiritual life. I experienced changes in all three. Amazingly, each change was for the better, though the daily confusion was simply too great for me to know this until quite recently.

When I began to sketch this book in October 1992, I was still early in a healing process that had already involved months of hospitalization and would require many more months of outpatient therapy and continuing therapy at home. My writing was almost indecipherable and took no particular direction: I was writing because I am a writer.

Then, for inspiration's sake, a friend loaned me the newly published memoir of a top-level editor with one of America's major news magazines. The book concerned his quadruple bypass. I don't remember the title, and I won't embarrass the author by mentioning his name. But I do recall the tone of his opening, which was a bit like this:

The murky day dawned dark and purple.

Well, no, thank you. I had written more than enough "purple" in my soap-opera-writing days.

My book would be different.

FIRST

The tone would be, well, not exactly breezy, perhaps, because the story includes many tense and serious moments that require total sobriety. No, I would tell my story in the same way that my wife, Mary Michael, and I have learned to deal with major life crises at home: to try in every way possible (and there are many ways possible) to find the humor in it. But I wouldn't do this the way writer/editor Norman Cousins did in a book about his own illness. His thesis, if I recall correctly, was that laughter heals, and so he would summon his own healing powers, for example, by renting Laurel and Hardy films. This is fine.

Being of the tongue-in-cheek generation that produced *Saturday Night Live* and *One Flew over the Cuckoo's Nest*, I also had the idea to acknowledge the healing power of laughter, but as directed toward *oneself.* Humor became, in fact, a legitimate way of dealing with just about any problem that might otherwise overwhelm. In using humor as my book's underlying philosophy, I hoped that a reader might be able to say, in effect,

"Hell, if this guy finds humor in his own brain damage, well, maybe I can learn to deal with my troubled romance. Or my broken leg. Or my failure to get a raise. Or my dead parakeet." Whatever.

SECOND

Physical problems, while they certainly existed, would not be discussed in depth. This would bring me too close to the soap opera turf I so wanted to avoid. So came another stricture: no Capra-like moments involving my own life's version of some dewy-eyed Jimmy Stewart cheering me on during early therapy: "Aw, gosh, Pete, c'mon! Ya know ya can do it! All ya gotta do is believe in yerself!" Such moments may be valid, even inspirational. But they were for other books by other people.

THIRD

I would report the psychological healing that had shown me the sweetness of a father who existed in a world far removed from my own, but whose approval I seemed to have spent a lifetime craving and who, however innocently, had laid the foundation for a mind-searing depression. This proved to be a major personal story that unfolded even as I wrote. Only later could I see that my little moments with Dad and my dog—moments I'd merely written as a *leitmotif*—were actually elements that had begun to form a most extraordinary healing.

FOURTH

I would report the extraordinary spiritual healing that finally warmed up this old atheist's long, cold winter without God. I would tell of my phenomenal near-death experience—in itself a possible book. But NDE literature is well-rutted turf, and, while my own experience was unique and important enough to share, I also wished to avoid overt evangelism and mysticism.

These would be my parameters. I liked them.

The resulting book, dealing largely with brain injury, often describes behavior whose memory may not be welcome to some of those involved. I have, therefore, taken extraordinary lengths to disguise identities. To that extent, some details at Gaylord Hospital, a hospital for patients of traumatic brain injury (TBI) at which most of my recovery took place, became partly fictionalized, while special care was taken to depict overall impressions of the world of brain injury as I experienced them.

Considering my own mental state during my early recovery, I must also concede that certain incidents could not have occurred precisely as reported. The retelling is based on how I, struggling with my own troubled brain, saw them. What's more, my story is told from memories of what I saw via that troubled brain, a factor that provides an even further remove. And most "journal" entries in the text are reconstructed to give form to scattershot notes and bits of confused information concocted by a gravely injured man struggling desperately to comprehend his world. Nevertheless, all events and characters remain firmly rooted in real, definable incidents and in the most solid memories to be conjured of that most confusing time.

I also changed the names and certain characteristics of the Gaylord staff to ward off any possibility of embarrassment to these highly committed, deeply caring professionals.

A very few of my early impressions occurred not at Gaylord, but at Stony Brook University Hospital, where I underwent brain surgery and spent the earliest days of recovery. (In my very earliest memories I still cannot distinguish between the two institutions.) And two minor characters are based on fellow patients at Long Island's Center for Rehabilitation, where I attended outpatient therapy for several months following hospitalization. For the sake of cohesion, I have set all such events and characters at Gaylord, where most of the story actually did occur.

* * *

In addition to those 2,500,000 Americans hospitalized with traumatic brain injury since my own experience, there are many more who were hospitalized before me whose lives remain disrupted, in some cases permanently.

I have walked the same halls, worked the same therapeutic devices, ridden the same wheelchairs, perceived the same upside-down world. I know what their disabilities are, and it is my hope that this book may begin to illuminate the world of confusion, fear, loneliness, and displacement that, humorous moments aside, are the reality of those so afflicted.

If I have told the story of brain injury well enough to make some positive difference, however minor, in the lives of these and others, I will have told it well, indeed.

That alone would make these four years of daily—often difficult—writing worthwhile.

ACKNOWLEDGMENTS

Foremost thanks and deepest gratitude go to my tenacious and indefatigable literary agent, the extraordinary Kay Kidde, who stuck resolutely by, refusing to let me lose hope in my book even though three agents had already walked away, feeling that the original material was simply too confused and disjointed. It was (and so, evidently, was I). Frequent bouts of intense mental confusion, memory loss, and my just not "getting" things had made me a pretty tough client, to be sure. Kay, however, understood that the raw material was essentially there; my problem was one of organization. She troubleshot that first, rough manuscript, telling me (without insulting me) where it did and didn't make sense. Then she left me alone. Following her suggestions, I moved chapters, eliminated extraneousness, and rewrote the unintelligible until, finally, I found continuity and, with it, a voice. Kay's associate, Laura Langlie, was also a major support in many ways, including bringing my work to the attention of *Men's Health* magazine, which published an early excerpt.

My good friend, Peter Majestro, helped, frequently and

without complaint, with my many computer problems (many generated by my own confusion) until I could work for several hours daily without glitches or hassles.

I must also acknowledge the Extension Program of Southampton College for making it possible for me to work with the excellent young student Patricia Fontana for several hours each week in my home. Patti quickly understood my special requirements and demands. She helped organize weekly, then daily, goals and step-by-step instructions and written reminders of tasks. Amazingly, she never lost her temper or her cool. Joann Cullinan of New York State's VESID (Vocational and Educational Services for Individuals with Disabilities) cooperated with Southampton College in making Patti's services available while providing additional support wherever possible. My two editors at Hazelden, Caryn Pernu and Betty Christiansen, were wonderful to work with, each making difficult work seem light due to their easygoing grace, wit, and charm, all of which may also be said of the trade publisher Dan Odegard and Senior Manuscript Editor Cathy Broberg. And in Westhampton Beach there is an extraordinary woman—Judi Lunn—who performed all my initial typing not only flawlessly but for free. Judi, I would discover later, had coincidentally been on her job as dispatcher with the local volunteer ambulance service and had been first to respond to Bertel Bruun's call for help when he discovered me collapsed on my living room floor. Additionally, I would discover only after insisting upon seeing her manuscript, Judi is an excellent memoirist with her own fascinating and challenging life story to tell.

In a more personal way I must first thank my mother, Alice, and father, Peter, for whom I have the profoundest love and appreciation; my children, Matthew and Emily Kate, whose strength and courage filled me with pride; my sister, Patricia, and her husband, Carmine, for their unfailing love, reliable presence, and support; my wife's family: her mother, Della Rinaldi, and her aunts Emma and Mary; her siblings Eugene and Dorothy, who raced to Mary Michael's side; her older sister Regina, who responded quickly and faithfully despite geographical distance; her in-laws, Paul, Marci, and Bill; her cousins Regina Krisky and Mary Jane Franco, who gave so freely of their time and resources in their rush to help; and the long list of her other relatives and childhood friends who rushed to assistance in so many important ways.

Sincere acknowledgment also to the volunteers of the Westhampton Beach War Memorial Ambulance Service; the emergency staff at Central Suffolk Hospital, which provided initial analysis and stabilization; the crew and paramedics of the Long Island MedEvac Helicopter Service, who safely transported me for emergency brain surgery; the staff of Stony Brook University Hospital, especially expert neurosurgeon Dr. Magdy Shady and his team of first-rate professionals; the rehab staff of that fine institution, especially Suzanne, Tom, and the many other professionals, surnames unknown, who were responsible for my earliest therapy; the dedicated and determined staff of Gaylord Hospital, especially Dr. Lack, Anne, Marianne, and the fine nursing staff as well as Joan, Marilyn, Susan, Jim, and the numerous other therapists; the Long Island staff of the Center for Rehabilitation; and my inventive, reliable, and wholly professional home therapist, Cheryl Schlitt.

The strongest personal acknowledgment and gratitude is due to Norene and Bob Gargiula, Connie and Rex Faar, Ralph and Jessie Nathan, all of whom halted their lives to join my wife and family in sitting vigil on the first and darkest night; to my aunt Florence Mahony and her husband, Brian, who aided my family at the speed of light, then stayed with them, and who, some six years later, may still be relied upon.

A debt of gratitude is also owed to the many, many people of

Westhampton. My pals Vic Levy and Bennett Brokaw were at our door that first night with offers of help. Our neighbor and attorney, Donald Noonan, straightened the extraordinary tangle of legal, insurance, and other household papers I'd left behind. Our dry cleaners, Popi and Nick, stubbornly refused any payment for their services for a period of a year or more. Many in Westhampton's real estate community rallied to our assistance in preparing to sell our house despite a very tough market: Sue Werntgen, also in real estate, found us an affordable rental on the water in nearby Quogue. Our wonderful friend Sunny Miller took my entire family, pets included, into her home during a lengthy interim, as did Bob and Norene Gargiula, who were helpful in so very many ways; Dr. Bertel Bruun, the dear friend whose quick action saved my life, also took time from his own writing to take me on long country walks to restore my stamina; his wife, Dr. Ruth Bruun, who may also have saved my life somewhat earlier by rescuing me from depression, welcomed us into her home during evacuations from Westhampton's violent winter storms, as did Dotson Rader and Richard Zoerinck. Peter Majestro helped me spiritually by picking me up for early mass twice weekly, then lingering for weighty philosophical discussions and bagels; Ralph Nathan took me for lunch each week, helping to restore abilities, such as they are, in interpersonal communication and even, perhaps, in wit; Mary Michael's (and my) dear friends Betty and Richard Schlein defined the term *generosity* in a thousand ways. The congregations of Immaculate Conception, Westhampton Presbyterian, and Beach Methodist all deserve my thanks for their prayers, as does the resplendent new Westhampton Synagogue. Peter and Diana Marbury were there for all of us, as they had been over twenty years of friendship. Many people brought wonderful dinners to my wife and kids during their first two months of my illness. And the following, some of whom have been mentioned in other contexts, issued a rallying call to our assistance: Eleanor Esposito, Betty Schlein, Richard Schlein, Candy Brokaw, Bennett Brokaw, Carol Oliveri, Miriam Gallacher, Joanna Ferraro-Levy, Norene Gargiula, Bob Gargiula, Peggy Johnson, Greta Hedburg, Charles Hedburg, Barbara Hope, Donald Gaiti, Ralph Nathan, Jessie Nathan.

Because of these and of all who answered their call, who sent me the many dozens of get-well wishes (Karol and George Mantell sent at least one weekly), or who proved in other ways that humans can be pretty terrific (ranging from Edward Urbanello and Carel Deleeuw's delivery of a surprise Christmas tree to the dozens of community members honoring me undeservingly with the 1993 Westhampton Writers Festival award), I will forever remember this blessed and most extraordinary community. Thank you.

CRACKING UP

1

The Night I Brought the House Down

It is safe to say I had become a successful writer.

Not colossally successful. Not wildly successful.

Successful.

Mostly, I had worked in theatre, which provided no income for the best efforts, and in television, which provided prodigious amounts for the least. In the end, it all seemed to balance.

My first play, *The Interview,* which I wrote at age twenty-four, was originally produced by Gene Frankel at the now-defunct Mercer Arts Center, once known as the Lincoln Center of off-Broadway. Mercer had housed such original hit productions as *One Flew over the Cuckoo's Nest* and *El Grande De Coca Cola,* in addition to works by established playwrights like Lorraine Hansberry and hit revivals of such masters as Shaw and Ibsen.

In addition to a handful of two-hundred-seat auditoriums, the Mercer Arts Center contained several smaller "studio" theatres of sixty or seventy seats as well as spaces for rehearsals and acting classes conducted by Viveca Lindfors. There was also the Gene Frankel Theatre Workshop, where I, along with several dozen other young playwrights and directors, cut my theatre teeth. A seventies-style boutique and a cabaret served as a kind of underground home to many burgeoning artists. Regulars who had "made it" in show business were honored with directors chairs bearing their names. In the glory days of the early seventies, the chairs bore names such as A. Pacino, L. Minnelli, M. Jagger, B. Jagger, J. Lennon, and Y. Ono. Lennon and Ono lived a short block away from my wife, Mary Michael, and me in those Nixon days when Lennon still faced deportation and the couple had not yet moved uptown to the Dakota. Their next-door neighbor was Bella Abzug, whose solid liberal credentials were apparent in the very name of her father's Manhattan business, The Live and Let Live Butcher Shop.

Mary Michael and I lived at the top of a two-hundred-year-old brownstone. Our downstairs neighbor, actor Gary Goodreau, moved in after an earlier tenant, a primal scream therapist who regularly sent bloodcurdling shrieks shattering through our floorboards, was asked to leave.

Gary's wife, Annie, ran a theatre program for prisoners called Captive Audience. The two had lots of parties, a practice Mary Michael and I appreciated since we were invariably invited. Their New York theatre guests might include Peter Boyle, Barbara Harris, the ubiquitous Sarah Miles, and others. Gary appeared, along with Alice Playton and then-unknowns Chevy Chase and John Belushi, in *National Lampoon's Lemmings,* a hilarious off-Broadway send-up of Woodstock.

At the neighborhood laundry (where one of us would inevitably borrow soap or bleach from the other), I would occasionally meet John Wood, also an unknown at the time.

It was that kind of neighborhood.

One might also run into these people at the Mercer during a spontaneous jam among John, Yoko, Mick, Bianca, or some combination of them and others. If it was your lucky night (usually well after midnight), and you were at the Mercer, you experienced one of the defining moments of the early seventies.

The Mercer Arts Center was housed on the first two floors of the old Broadway Central Hotel, which a century earlier had been at the epicenter of New York splendor, its elegant second-floor dining rooms and private parlors hosting regulars like Diamond Jim Brady, Lillian Russell, P. T. Barnum, and Jenny Lind. Now the old private function rooms, their multitiered crystal chandeliers removed and their ornately detailed, gilded mantelpieces painted over in flat theatre black, served as smaller studio theatres. Gene Frankel's workshop was in such a space.

There, working with the great Lou Gilbert, Mark Gordon, and other first-rate talents, I was able to finish work on *The Interview,* which so pleased Mr. Frankel that he decided to present it as a workshop production under strict Actors Guild guidelines. This meant, among other restrictions, that we were permitted a total of twelve performances, that the audience was limited to no more than sixty souls, that actors would be reimbursed for travel and meal expenses, and that ticket prices could not exceed three dollars.

Frankel also thought that the critics should have a look at my piece, especially the *New York Times.* Problem was, the *Times* did not cover off-off-Broadway. Frankel was persistent, however, and I, myself, nagged their theatre department regularly. I wheedled. I whined. I pleaded. To shut me up, I think, the folks up at the "Power and the Glory" finally decided it was time for a good look at this growing phenomenon called off-off-Broadway. They sent a critic named Howard Thompson.

Thompson loved it.

"One of the finest theatre presentations in town," he wrote. "*The Interview* catches fire and touches the heart." He concluded with a power quote: "*The Interview* is one to remember."

Then came other critics. Emory Lewis hailed, "A major new playwright."

Bill Raidy, under the headline, "A Playwright Is Born," said, "Another reviewer called *The Interview* a play to remember. I say it is one that must not be forgotten. And remember the name: Peter Swet." Heady stuff.

Was this really true? I kept thinking. *Was this really me?*

At Frankel's workshop the phones rang. And rang. Frankel booked the show for another run and put his assistant on as a full-time reservationist.

On the afternoon of our reopening, I wandered the short distance from our Greenwich Village apartment to catch the final rehearsal. This time *Newsweek* and *Time* would be present, I'd been told, along with international media, many agents, and perhaps a few main-stem producers.

But by the time I got there, trouble was brewing.

I found a bewildered Frankel at his desk, his head in one hand and a glass of Stolichnaya in the other.

"What's the matter, Gene?"

"Go look at the theatre."

Walking the few feet from his office to our little auditorium's entrance, I noticed a small but growing cone of plaster dust on the floor beneath the doorway's header beam. The beam itself was creaking and groaning, apparently unhinged by God-knows-what forces at work in the old building.

"Looks like that floor above us could be in trouble," I said.

"Trouble? It could come crashing down any moment."

There wasn't much choice. I removed the various elements of my very simple set, placing them in a grand old hallway.

Next came thoughts of any people who might be living in the single-room occupancy hotel above us.

Frankel agreed that the last thing we needed was my opening night audience to be supplemented by the crashing arrival of an army of surprised welfare recipients and various other shocked hotel denizens caught *en déshabillé* as they came tumbling onto the tailor shop set of *The Interview.* Frankel would make plans to open that night in another space within the Mercer Arts Center while I ran around the block to the faded grandeur of the hotel's Broadway entrance.

Feeling foolish and alarmist, I entered the thick yellow-and-smoke atmosphere of a once-grand lobby that was now furnished with threadbare carpeting, torn cotton drapes, and soiled, overused furniture.

Locating a laconic young man who seemed to be in charge, I carefully dusted off my best college Spanish and explained the problem.

He assured me he would vacate the rooms, thus ensuring safety, then proceeded to scratch his privates and locate quarters for the soda machine. Realizing that he might not be the most reliable party to lay out an evacuation plan, I called the police myself and then went back up to Frankel, whose phones still rang wildly.

"Problem solved," Frankel said. "We open in the Shaw."

"But that's almost three hundred seats."

"Hear those phones?" he replied.

After walking the several blocks back to our apartment, I called my wife's office, untroubled by the remotest foreboding. I was reopening in the three-hundred-seat Shaw Arena. This would be the most exciting night in my young professional life, and my young wife, also sniffing success, dared to dream the Broadway dream along with me. Tonys and humble acceptance speeches and parties at Sardi's—if not surrounding this play, then certainly my next one—all seemed within grasp.

And then the phone rang. It was Ted Story, friend and director.

"Peter, have you been to the theatre since five o'clock?"

"No, not since around two. Why?"

"Well, it's gone!"

"What?"

I hung up and raced back to Mercer Street where, instead of the familiar old Mercer Arts Center, I found . . . rubble.

The entire building—all of it—had crumbled to the ground. Gone forever.

Across Mercer Street, near a row of parked cars that had been crushed by falling brick and mortar, stood Viveca Lindfors, upset by the world of theatre memories that had just crashed before her.

Farther down stood my cast of two—Joey Fitter and Richard Creamer—standing among a group of playwright friends. One of them, Mike Zettler, had arrived shortly before the collapse. He described it for me:

"Everyone was involved with whatever work they were doing when the whole damned building hit about an eight on the Richter, and *ka-whoosh!* came the first stage of collapse. I tell you, Peter, steam pipes burst, gas mains were exposed, chandeliers came loose, and half the glass from that Versailles Hall of Mirrors came dancing off those walls.

"Gene was terrific. 'Everybody out!' he shouted. 'Walk, don't run. Use the stairs, not the elevator.' Well, we all came in a steady line down that grand staircase like we were playing a scene from *Tosca* or something; then we slowly marched out of the lobby and across the street here, when it sounded like a twister was hitting. We all turned to see the entire center coming down—just like that." He snapped his fingers. "Gone."

"Anyone hurt?"

"Not a soul. Someone called the cops. They cleared everyone out before the first collapse."

I didn't say a word, lest I wind up accused of involvement in some bizarre Weathermen or Chicago 7 plot (the Weathermen had recently blown up the townhouse next to Dustin Hoffman's on my own street, West 11th, and, as I said, it *was* the Nixon era).

Mary Michael and I have long believed in laughing, wherever possible, at our own travails, reasoning that the alternative is often simply beyond bearing. Such was the case here, where our young hopes and dreams were dashed in a single, decisive shot from fate.

"Let's face it," the *New York Post*'s Joyce Wadler quoted yours truly as saying during our interview, "I'm the only playwright who brought the house down before the house ever opened."

Our production fumbled afterward, wandering from the Actors Playhouse to the Theatre DeLys (now the Lucille Lortel) to the Bouwerie Lane, even doing a brief stint as part of a fundraiser in a legitimate Broadway house. But the production was shot. Months later, our aging co-lead Joey Fitter, a stage veteran who had placed all his hopes in this one last chance for acting success, methodically placed a plastic bag over his head after downing a bottle of roach poison.

The Interview continued on in many ways, however. Published by Dramatists Play Service, it was included in Chilton Books' *Best Short Plays of 1975* and went on to more than 150 professional and amateur radio and television productions throughout the United States, Canada, Europe, and Australia. In 1985, a television version with Eli Wallach was produced, but, unfortunately, it never aired. I possess the last tape. Whenever I run into Wallach, which happens occasionally, he nags me about providing new work.

"Well, Peter," this fine actor and extraordinary man will say, "don't you have another play for me yet?"

Some day I will.

Despite the failure of that first production, however, life still seemed young, bursting with choices and boundless with opportunity.

Shortly after the collapse, I was offered a job writing for an NBC soap opera, *Another World,* which I accepted in the face of disparagement from Greenwich Village theatre friends. Mary Michael was pregnant with our first child, and, while I loved the theatre, I also loved the idea of my family having a future.

In addition, there soon came comedy work with Jerry Stiller and Anne Meara, perhaps the two finest human beings I have known in the world of show business. Then came a terrific three-year stint with *Sesame Street,* where I learned to write "up" to my very best abilities for three-year-olds instead of "down" (as producers seemed to require) for soap opera audiences.

It's not that I hated soaps—no one who makes a generous living out of them should. But I found it impossible to juggle my own stringent playwriting criteria with market forces which dictated that the major job of the writer, after increasing the size of the audience, was to provide that audience with an entertaining way to fill the spaces between commercials. Many people perform this job well, then take the money and run. God knows it's what television is all about.

But despite the Writers Guild award and Emmy citations I

received for my soap opera work, God help us, the world of soaps just wasn't for me.

* * *

It feels odd to punch the word *God* on my computer keyboard. It's a word I had rarely used, except in derisive terms, since declaring myself an atheist at age nineteen. I was naturally cocksure of the Nothingness That Is There and could easily argue most opposing views under the table.

Or so I thought.

After all, who needed God? At the point at which my story begins, I was a young writer at the top of his mountain, or at least on his way there. I'd learned the worlds of theatre, television, and even journalism on my own. I'd gotten my name in the big New York papers without a well-off, sophisticated family and without big friends in the biz. Furthermore, I'd been through Catholic schools all my life, so I knew the drill about God and had done pretty damn well for a working-class kid from Ozone Park, Queens.

Those who had performed my television and stage work (in addition to Jerry Stiller, Anne Meara, and Eli Wallach) included Gilda Radner, Judy Collins, Buffy Sainte-Marie, Luke Perry, Joan Lunden, Richard Dean Anderson, Celeste Holm, John Ireland, Tammy Grimes, R2D2, C-3P0, Kermit the Frog, Big Bird, and the Muppets.

Those I would eventually interview and profile as a journalist with *Parade* magazine included Sean Connery, Loretta Young, Billy Joel, Maureen O'Hara, Dan Aykroyd, and Charlie Sheen, and I would travel throughout the United States and Europe to cover them.

My income had become quite healthy: I had a terrific, very pretty, and very, very funny wife; a terrific son; a terrific daughter; and a beautiful house in Long Island's fabled Hamptons.

I also had had the honor of meeting and dealing with such well-known American writers as Budd Schulberg, Kurt Vonnegut, Norman Mailer, Dotson Rader, Marsha Norman, Lanford Wilson, Terrence McNally, Wilfred Sheed, Pete Hamill, and Betty Friedan.

While belonging to a generation filled with Reagan-era yuppies, a fact that influenced our purchase of a Westhampton house we couldn't really afford, my wife and I possessed what people still called values. We marched on the United Nations, actively opposed an unjust and inhumane war, struggled against nuclear power, segregation, and bigotry, sent money to a host of causes, and did our very best to Fight the Good Fight while, wherever possible, helping the unfortunate and the dispossessed.

Mary Michael had established her own increasingly successful interior design firm, M. M. Rinaldi Associates (using her birth name), and had been receiving ever-increasing attention both in the Hamptons and New York.

By 1992, my sandy-haired son, Matt, was eighteen, a good-looking boy of brute size but of gentle nature and good humor, a fine guitar player with high hopes for a future in jazz. He was headed for college.

My pretty, ash-blond daughter, Emily Kate, was fifteen, played the piano, had a deep interest in literature, and was considering offers from prep schools for her high school sophomore year.

Both kids were conscientious citizens, loyal friends, and good neighbors with firmly rooted morals. We had a "good" car and a station wagon, a dog, a cat, and the usual assortment of hamsters, lizards, and goldfish. And friends. We had many,

many good friends. Ours was a pretty good version of an American nuclear family living the American dream.

Who needed God? We had it all.

We had it all, that is, until a few shattering moments one gorgeous early spring morning when, like the Mercer Arts Center, it was all suddenly gone.

2

Nice Day for a Brain Hemorrhage

The truth be told, though, life wasn't completely a picnic up to that fine spring day. Like the Mercer Arts Center, my life began to crack and crumble well before the entire house came down. This began in 1988, when a television writers strike put me out of work and forced me to face that plague of our post-Freudian, boomer-oriented society: clinical depression.

Much of my depression stemmed from the fact that I'd spent so much of my professional life in the lucrative but, for me, psychically destructive world of television soap opera instead of heeding my very first creative writing professor, Sarah Zimmerman, who'd issued this most important ukase in our very first class:

"Never, I repeat, never be a prostitute for the *Reader's Digest*." Even we hopelessly green University of Dayton sophomores understood that she referred to the selling of the soul, and "Don't be a prostitute for the *Reader's Digest*" became a catchphrase and battle cry embracing all our sophomoric ideals.

If only I'd listened.

* * *

After I lost my job, my good friend Dotson Rader, a journalist and best-selling author, helped me to get work as a writer for *Parade,* then endlessly attempted to convince me to keep a daily journal, on the theory that my travels and interviews might one day either yield a book or be used in one. Unlikely as this seemed at the time, I nevertheless began a journal the winter of 1991, during a trip to Spain to interview Sean Connery.

I had met Sean Connery earlier that year at a cocktail party on the set of *Medicine Man* in the jungles of Mexico, where I had gone to interview his co-star, Lorraine Bracco, and succeeded in convincing Connery that I should also interview him for a *Parade* article. Connery is notorious for hostility toward the press, and so I was rather proud of myself for having the guts to approach him with business while everyone else, including Bracco's own two young daughters by then-husband Harvey Keitel and two dozen primeval-looking child extras, was busy voguing. He referred me to his agent to work out details, a process that took several months since it involved busy schedules and complex travel arrangements. Some of this is reflected in my journal entries:

> *December 1991.* Finally met Connery. Tough going at first, since his agent screwed up our time and place, so I was sipping café con leche under some olive trees in the beautiful Hotel Marbella gardens while he was waiting—steamed, I was sure—at the hotel desk. Surprisingly, he proved not to be angry or even gruff. He was actually fun to be with, with a quick, deep laugh and a love of good stories. But the man's no dope. When he sensed me getting too close to his hot buttons, he "suddenly" recalled a chiropractic appointment in Málaga, an hour's drive, and

was gone in an instant. Luckily, I'd already gathered enough for a good profile and was by this time just taking in some icing.

But I was not faithful to my journal every day, as Dotson had prescribed. It seemed vain and self-centered to keep a journal. And I was too busy. So I would write only an occasional entry such as the following, later that spring, in which I finally absorbed some unintentional advice from Joan Rivers:

March 8, 1992. This warm-to-tepid weather makes it impossible to get up a head of writing steam. Even indoors one can hear pounding surf accented by a cacophony of birds chattering excitedly over early arrival at their summer homes in the Hamptons. Sitting at our long dining-room table, gazing through multiple French panes onto a garden filled with sap-tipped trees, it seems hard to remember that I am a working writer: that is, one accustomed to the long, grueling hours of television work as well as the complexities, inconveniences, and fascination of traveling on a story. I need a project desperately. Maybe this journal will provide the jump start I need to get down to the serious business of earning a living. We'll see.

Later: The sun's too high and the world's too beautiful to enjoy from behind anything, including multiple French panes. And so, surrendering to this defiantly balmy winter day, I have moved legal pads, coffee, pens, journal entries, staplers, etc., to the opposite side of those windows to work in the outdoor warmth (yes, in March!) of this gorgeous, sun-filled day. My wife, my Mary Michael, just passed by to blow a kiss and wave at me on her way to some series of chores for the interior design firm she runs with her partner, Norene McKenna. Across the garden on the other side of a swimming pool, which will be open for the season in a mere sixty days, our little dog, Spike, jumps and bites at a swarm of preseason gnats, alternately dropping to roll around a lawn that is a crawl with its own swarm of preseason fleas.

At the edge of the large, sunny, blue slate patio, where a thick row of pink impatiens will soon flourish, lie various sections of broken garden hose and other reminders of my chores for today: I am to pick up a hose repair kit, for example, and one of those little plastic Siamese connectors that will divert water into a hose attached to my "squirting turtle," a whimsical piece of statuary that fills the pool while providing one and all with the carefree illusion of frolicking in turtle spit.

The naming of Spike, incidentally, had nothing to do with the dog of the same name owned by Joan Rivers, with whom I spent considerable time during recent interview sessions in Atlantic City and New York.

As I now pull out of my own goddamn depression, I sometimes think of Rivers and of the depression suffered by her husband, Edgar, who killed himself in a Philadelphia hotel room. People still think that Rivers was in some way responsible for his death and that she is, in private, some god-awful bitch.

She is not.

It was her story involving the love she obviously had for Edgar, in fact, that prevented me from sticking a gun in my mouth or from overloading on drugs in some out-of-town hotel room as he had done a year or two earlier.

Rivers's residual pain and anger were still apparent as she vividly described his slow descent into the howling maw of depression.

"The man was in agony," she said, "but he was so tight-lipped that no one knew how bad it was, not even his psychiatrist."

At the time of this interview, Rivers was in her first year of a new daytime talk show and was grittily determined to succeed.

"For Edgar," she told me, tears in full flow.

Gasping for quick infusions of oxygen, she angrily pounded the table between us. While she still loved her late husband, she was furious with him for taking such a selfish way out and for not considering the devastation that suicide would create for their daughter, Melissa, who was a teen at the time and who required extensive psychiatric assistance in reconstructing her shattered young life.

The suicide option, it became obvious, was not for anyone with kids.

It also became apparent that those suicidal fantasies of mine were symptoms of a real illness that required real, and immediate, treatment. I could not possibly do to my offspring what Edgar, however inadvertently, had done to his.

I sought help.

Now, after having received that help from a psychiatrist friend, Ruth Bruun, depression has lifted and what has emerged is a healthily neurotic American male in his late forties, determined to enjoy a life filled with love and the continued exploration of as-yet-unfulfilled promise.

I've been looking for a book subject. Depression's been covered, notably by William Styron, whose title alone, *Darkness Visible*, is perhaps the closest one can come to describing the illness. But maybe I can provide another viewpoint. After three produced plays, a few good seasons on *Sesame Street*, a lot of good comedy for

Stiller and Meara, plus a load of misery for the soaps and more recent success as a journalist, it's high time for that first book.

But what about?

* * *

That winter was extraordinarily mild on eastern Long Island. I was filled with an urge to write, to work, to be a fully productive father, husband, and human being after my bout with unemployment and depression.

Dotson, who'd become a very good and very dear friend to my entire family by now, was in the habit of stopping over regularly to work on a movie screenplay to be pitched to his friend, producer Howard Rosenman. Dotson is quite well known among New York society, at whose most glittering events he is the frequent escort of Patricia Kennedy Lawford. As a result, he has many, many influential friends in society, publishing, and film.

Dotson is a converted Catholic. He is also an avowed, outspoken gay man, secure enough in his lifestyle and convictions to not mind my writing about this. The inherent conflict of Catholicism and homosexuality was something about which I'd often wondered, and I recall planning to question him about it that day when he came over to work on our screenplay. Aside from my recent interview of Connery and a recent profile Dotson had done on Milton Berle, he and I were each enduring lengthy dry periods in our work, and each hoped the other would help induce a creative flow. My entry from that day was written moments after he called to remind me of our appointment. The call came just moments before my own life and that of my family would be forever changed:

March 25, 1992. D. just called and will stop by to discuss our outline of the screenplay we're planning. The idea, his, involves the ultra-secret "40 Committee" alleged to be at the epicenter of our government. I like it.

When Dotson called, my brain had probably already begun to hemorrhage, though I hadn't the slightest indication.

Since there was no pain, no dizziness, no warning of any kind, it seems impossible that on that gorgeous morning my brain hemorrhage had begun even earlier: by the time, in fact, my darling Mary Michael kissed me good-bye on her way to an appointment "up island," which is the term we East End Long Islanders use, when we want to sound quaint and countrified, to describe areas farther to the west.

The first indication that something was amiss occurred during a phone conversation with another writer friend, Mike Miller, who called faithfully every morning.

Mike was about three years older than my dad, though he would never admit this, and was a firm, fine friend. When we met ten years earlier, he smoked like what my old Yankee grandma would have called a Pittsburgh chimney. Soon he suffered emphysema so debilitating that he had to travel with an emergency oxygen tank in his car. This couldn't dampen his *joie de vivre*, however, or his outrageously skewed sense of humor.

Telephone chats with Mike never failed to be hilarious, and today was no exception. As we joked and teased, though, my speech inexplicably began to slow down, sounding garbled and confused. While I explained the "40 Committee" idea Dotson and I were working on, this became apparent:

"We're bworkring on a movie about a trop stecret group called the Frtra Cmrotrot."

"You're what?"

I repeated, broken sound by broken sound. Mike sounded annoyed.

"Peter, either your mouth or your head is full of crap. I can't understand you."

I tried again, but this time my voice was distorted and hollow, like a jet pilot hitting Mach 2 in mid-conversation. Mike, not realizing something was wrong, was waiting for some sort of punch line and becoming impatient with my nonsense.

"Come on, will you? Quit fooling around."

But I wasn't fooling. My voice dragged out, achingly slow and distorted.

"Mrike, I'm not bfrooblring," I insisted. He could not, of course, comprehend.

I panicked.

What is this? I yelled inwardly. *What the hell is going on?*

Forcing away fears of anything unlikely, I drew myself under control. Thinking patterns seemed fine and clear, after all. But when these patterns were processed into verbal expression, they couldn't squeeze properly through my mouth, tongue, and teeth. I sounded, to myself, like an old 78 RPM record switched suddenly to play on 33, or like HAL in *2001: A Space Odyssey,* who, in the memorable scene when Keir Dullea disassembles him, starts to sing "Daisy, Daisy."

"Mike," I asked, taking pains with each syllable, "do you hear anything wrong with my speech?"

Mike, while totally reliable for support, did not relish individual responsibility and so seemed afraid of saying something wrong. My question put him on the spot.

"Well, uhm, let's see," he began as I visualized the dramatic, Jack Benny–like trip his slender fingers were undoubtedly making down his sad, basset hound face. This trip, repeated several times a day, began at his temples. From there his fingertips would flutter liquidly down, lingering languorously at his cheek before crossing a pair of perennially pouting, 1930s Jackie Cooper lips. The overall gesture was humorously endearing, adding to the impression of some deeply perplexed state in which Mike seemed always to reside.

"Yeah, I see what you mean," he continued, apparently agreeing although not at all certain.

Then, "No, no, maybe not."

Then, "Yeah, sure, I hear what you mean, you'd better do something."

Then, "Nah, nah, nope."

Then, with a sigh and a final resolve as I could again envision those long, ladylike fingers lapping at his cheeks:

"I don't know."

I was getting nowhere with dear, indecisive Mike.

Then he asked a question that made me feel frozen in ice.

"Peter," he said, "have you been drinking?"

Mike thus told me, without the need to commit himself, that something was very wrong, indeed.

And growing worse.

Doctors say that memory of such brain trauma is exceedingly rare, but the drama of this moment and those that followed is so deeply burrowed into my skull that it is easy to reconstruct details, including my own thought patterns.

Mike sees something is wrong! I remember thinking. *He knows I don't drink alone and never in the morning. Why do I feel so woozy, fuzzy, not in control? My God, the phone! I can't hold on to it! It's slipping right out of my hand.*

Then, *Peter, you're being an ass. Of course you can hold the damned phone, just grab it! Just ...*

Thunk! came the hollow plastic sound as the force of life flew from my left hand and the phone dropped to the kitchen butcher block.

Why can't I hold it? Why can't I pick it up?

"Mike! Mike, are you still there?"

"What happened? You dropped the phone?"

"It . . . it just pfeww out of my hand! I can't . . . I can't muff it. I'm not taljking fwight . . . Mike! Mike, my God! I'm pawwyzed! Somedwing's hoppning to me, Mike. Mike!"

"You want me to drive over?"

Yes! Yes, I want you to drive over is what I thought, but:

"No, it's probably nothing" is what I said, feeling foolish and not wanting him to drive the short distance from Remsenberg. Mike was hardly an accomplished, secure driver. And now, with the complications of emphysema and his addled state, I tried my best to reassure him.

But what was I to do about myself?

"Do you feel anything else? Your heart?" he asked.

"Heart's fine, I fwink!"

It's just this phone! I can't hold it! My fingers are like bent twigs. I can't move them! I can't move my arm! I try and nothing happens! Mike! I screamed inside my head, but:

"Mike," I muttered calmly enough to be understood, "I'd better drive to the hospital in Riverhead."

No!" he shouted, stunning me to attention with unaccustomed assertiveness. "Suppose something happens while you're driving? You can't do that!"

Mike's right, I thought. *I could lose consciousness or something and end up killing God knows how many people!* With this thought, someone or something outside myself took control of the left side of my body. The back of my left wrist drifted chinward, where it remained welded for several weeks.

I hung up quickly, assuring Mike that before driving I would call Bertel Bruun who, apart from being another writer friend and the husband of the psychiatrist who pulled me out of depression, is a neurologist. But I hated bothering Bertel with a question that seemed like an attempt at free medical advice. At the time, I didn't even know what a stroke was. Nor did I know that Bertel has spent his professional life helping stroke victims and had even founded the free stroke clinic at Harlem Hospital.

What I did know is that my only alternative was to take an eight-mile drive to the nearest hospital in Riverhead, risking an accident that might take any number of lives. Since my left hand was now useless, I lifted the phone off its wall cradle with my right and listened for the dial tone. I then laid the phone on the butcher block to dial with my right hand, and again took the receiver with my right hand when I heard a familiar, booming voice:

"Hello, this is the Bruun residence. . . ."

Shit! It's the goddamn answering machine! I screamed inside. I started to rummage for my car keys, determined to drive to the hospital, when suddenly . . .

"Hello, hold on, please," a live Danish accent cut in.

Hallelujah!

Able to speak more clearly at this point, I carefully told Bertel what had happened, building to the question of whether to drive to Riverhead, something I actually felt confident enough to do.

"Absolutely not," he insisted. "What you must do is this: Find yourself a good, sturdy chair, one where you are not likely to fall over. Stay in it without moving," he instructed, "and I will be there as quickly as possible. And Peter," he added before I hung up. "Most important. You must remember to unlatch the front door so I can get in."

Since I was in reasonably good health and still in my forties, a positive answer to my next question seemed unlikely. Nevertheless, I asked.

"Bertel," I said, feeling foolish and timid, "could I be having a stroke?"

His response was simple and quiet, though I can still hear it as if it had been shouted in reverb over the PA system of some mammoth Copenhagen used car lot.

"Yes," he said. "Now do as I told you, and don't forget to unlock the door. I will get there as quickly as possible."

My God! This is a stroke! my mind screamed as, carefully hanging up with my right hand, I determined to follow Bertel's instructions.

But Christ! It's getting worse! I shouted inside myself as the muscle group supporting my left shoulder collapsed and that bundle of twigs once known as my left hand coiled ever more tightly toward my chin. My left leg, also under alien control, turned to rubber and was suddenly two feet shorter than the right. Despite the most powerful efforts to regain authority over my own body parts, I could only sway and stumble, a dancing monkey unhinged and out of control.

What I didn't yet know was that because a blood vessel had burst within my right cerebral hemisphere, a blood clot had formed and was growing, squeezing aside living tissue and thereby knocking out the various systems controlled by that section of the brain. My left hand and arm were completely gone by this point, and control of my left leg was also on its way out.

What the hell? What's happening now? I yelled inside my head as my leg gave way, my left shoulder crashing painfully against the dining-room door frame. The impact sent my body rebounding to the right, causing another crash, though not as hard, to the opposite frame. There I remained for what seemed like several hours, bouncing back and forth in the doorway, my left shoulder in shattering pain.

Now I'm in a goddamn paddleball game. And I'm the ball!

The image I have of these moments is one of the *Titanic* as portrayed in *A Night to Remember*, its boilers and generators booming and exploding as they are knocked out one by one and slowly, slowly, the great ship goes down. On top deck, the ship's orchestra does not play "Nearer My God to Thee," but something closer to the 1970s Gloria Gaynor hit "I Will Survive," I think, because of my rigid determination to achieve the goal Bertel had set.

Extricated from my doorway demolition derby, I gained the dining room, a long, light-filled space furnished in yuppie English country pine. As I made my way down the length of the twelve-foot table, it became necessary to maul at chairs for support.

Crack! Crack! Crack! went several chairs, a set of wooden soldiers hit by cork and splayed recklessly on the hardwood floor.

Keep it going, Pete! Keep it up! You're almost at the entry!

Achieving the entry, I kept steady by clawing at the wall.

Keep going, man! Don't lose it now or you'll pass out on the floor and the kids will find you dead when they get home! You can't do that to them! Come on, now! Come on! Passing through the door frame into the living room, however, it happened again—*crack!*

But this time, it wasn't a wooden chair striking the floor.

It was my head striking the door frame.

Pain burned across my forehead and down the side of my face, and my vision began to blur. But I had reached the living room!

Something else was wrong, however. The simple country room with its white painted wooden walls and picturesque bay window had grown enormously since I last saw it that morning and was now approximately the length of the Sistine chapel.

And there, miles away at the other end where the finger of God touches the finger of Adam, lay my goal: the stuffed chair!

Grasping and pulling across this newly vast space, I made it to the chair, spun around, and flopped securely into it.

Then: *Wait a minute! No! No, this isn't possible! No!*

But it was true. I had forgotten to unlock the door for Bertel!

Okay, you have no choice.

I heaved a sigh, gritted my teeth, and started again down the nave of the Sistine. With head aching wildly and shoulder in shattering pain from those two collapses, my thoughts turned suddenly to my wife, my darling, my Mary Michael, and to my handsome young son and gorgeous daughter. Would I ever see them again?

Yes! Yes, goddamn it! There's no way I can do this to them! I won't!

This thought, repeated over and over, became the fuel that drove and propelled me, despite many more falls and stumbles down that vast, ethereal space. Upon reaching the door, I had to prop my body against the wall, a tricky effort, since all it really wanted to do was slide down that wall and onto the floor. The lock, magically, worked quite easily, leaving me triumphant as I turned to make the last long walk-crawl back to the chair—my one safe haven.

What awaited me was impossible to determine. But for now, my total focus was on that white chair I perceived as salvation, the only safe space in a room and a world that had turned, without warning, into a low-budget horror film.

After perhaps a two-minute period that felt like the better part of a morning, the upholstered, secure white chair was reached. I grabbed it and spun, finally able to quit fighting those alien powers, and—*yes!* The front door was unlocked and I was in a good, secure chair. *Okay, Bertel, I did it. I did all that you said and I'm ready for you, so come ahead!*

This final memory of that day is quite faint, especially considering that by this point, I had begun to fall into a coma. As I slowly blacked out, I felt I was tumbling, tumbling, like a skin diver in slo-mo or like one of our local harbor seals as it plops into the bay. Actually, I was sliding out of that nice, secure chair I had taken such pains to reach.

And I now believe that, as I slid from that chair onto the floor and into the deep, black pool of a coma, it was my love for my Mary Michael and my kids that caused me to do something I hadn't done since becoming that rather hard-nosed atheist in my university years. I also did it for fear of the unknown world that was suddenly before me, I know, but mostly it was for them:

I prayed.

3

Notes from the Loony Bin

Two months later, still hospitalized, I picked up the pen and legal pad Mary Michael brought for my journal and made an attempt to write, though the entry is quite troubled:

> *May 24, 1992, 6:00* A.M. Screaming and more screaming. Christ, won't this guy ever stop? Every damned morning, about an hour before sunrise. Yells the names of every person he's ever heard of, insisting they get him out of here. Poor guy. Thinks he's in some prison torture chamber or something. I have deliriums too. Bad ones.

It's pretty astonishing that I was able to write anything at this early stage of recovery (or ever again), but anyone who writes for a living understands that if you're a writer, you're a writer to the very core of your being. And what does a writer do? He writes!

The deliriums in question were not merely "bad ones," incidentally. They were living nightmares. Instead of being at Gaylord Hospital, one of the finest brain injury rehabilitation centers in the country, my mind had me in some back-alley joint where black marketeers were removing the internal organs of kidnapped patients. One night, I was convinced that all this yelling and screaming came from some poor guy who was having his liver removed the cost-effective way—without anesthesia.

This was so upsetting that many visits from many nurses could not calm me throughout the night. One of the nurses in our unit was John, a man with whom I never quite hit it off. John knew I didn't like him—it was obvious in my demeanor—and I was sure John didn't give a damn about me. On that occasion, however, he sat with me through the bloodcurdling night, parent to a forty-nine-year-old child, until, finally realizing no one was going to rip my stomach open, I nodded off. I remember asking a thousand questions and feeling soothed by my enemy's infinite patience and calm reassurance. John's patience and care were typical traits of Gaylord's staff, people who, I sometimes feel, raised me from the dead.

Now you may understand why this chapter is titled as it is, being compiled from my journal entries and reflecting my own false perceptions at the time. To illustrate this point, let me show you another entry from my journal:

> *May 28, 1992, morning.* The old screamer, whoever he is, is at it again. He started around 4:00 A.M. and just stopped about a minute ago. Almost 8:00 now. The attendants in this nuthatch have provided a detachable tray for my wheelchair so I can take meals in my room. Mary Michael, with whom I have once again fallen in love, long ago provided me with legal pads and writing equipment

so that, in addition to acting as a table for meals, the tray has become my writing desk.

Now, here is the same section as it appeared in my notebook before editing. Virtually every journal entry from this period needed rewriting. This will show you why:

> *May 28 1992.* Sonofabitch. Screaming, screaming. Every day wakes me up and it's still dark. Nuthouse nurses gave me this tray for eating. To early to eat but now I can write while jerk-o screams. Where's Mary? I love her like never but she can't be here. Kids can't be here. Right? Too far away. Right? She give me this yellow pad and pens. Knows I am a writer and must not give up! So see? I don't give up. Tray is a desk. I can write. See?

Yet at this point in my stay at Gaylord, I couldn't really write, having only begun to figure out just who and what I was and what I was doing there. If I had been able to give a play-by-play report of my condition and state of mind, it would have sounded something like this:

What *am* I doing here?

They tell me that my brain exploded.

Okay, okay, *exploded* may not be the official medical term, but now you know what a brain hemorrhage seems like from the inside.

Officially, I had what is referred to as a cerebrovascular "incident"; that is, a blood vessel burst in the right front section of my brain. The oxygen within the blood immediately began to form a blood clot that grew rapidly, bearing down, in my mind's eye, like that famous boulder racing through the tunnel in

Raiders of the Lost Ark. Brain cells were squashed out by the hundreds of thousands, with additional damage from the caustic effect of the blood. This necessitated immediate surgery.

Under the knife of a neurosurgeon, Dr. Magdy Shady, my scalp was partially shaved as prep for emergency surgery. The shaved portion was then carefully sliced and peeled back to expose the skull, a bone case of surprisingly yellow tone in its living state.

Following a pattern laid out and marked with the help of a brain scan, Dr. Shady cut into the portion of skull covering the clotted area (about two inches above the right brow and then several inches back) with an electric surgical saw gauged perfectly to the unvarying depth of the human skull. In this manner, what is literally a "skull cap" was formed, then removed and set aside, exposing the living brain so the still-growing clot could be surgically removed. The bleeding vessel was cauterized, the skull cap replaced, the skin flap resewn, and there you have it: the nickel version of brain surgery (and remember, kids, don't try this at home).

Although the surgery undoubtedly saved my life, much damage had already occurred. I awoke from a fifteen-day coma to discover that I was paralyzed on the left side. No movement. No sensation. No heat, no cold, no pain—nothing. Walking was out of the question; my left arm was completely useless, and there were many other effects. But I know I am most fortunate, indeed, since many who suffer this affliction are left in a far more challenging situation. Most die.

I have already spent two months in one hospital and now have to spend another couple of months at Gaylord. But it's not so bad. It took a couple of months, sure, but I have begun to walk again, at least a little, and I am taken out of my wheelchair each day to practice along a protected ramp in the gym. Soon I will be ready for a four-legged cane.

I get headaches that kick in two or three times a day, but it's not so bad, because usually a couple of Tylenol will take care of them. Same with this constant pain in my left shoulder where cartilage has begun to calcify. The shoulder must be given a painful "ranging" each morning. This is an exercise that prevents further calcification while breaking up any bone particles that have already formed. I get through it by telling everyone in the gym that I am going to scream my head off. And then I scream my head off. This forces us to laugh, and the unbearable becomes bearable.

My blood pressure runs all over the place, sometimes creating feelings of lethargy and sometimes of dizziness. This will straighten out in time.

I have a stamina problem that makes me feel as if I am no longer in my late forties, but suddenly in my seventies or eighties. Things ache, and a tired, worn-out feeling makes bed very attractive by eight or nine in the evening. This must be what it feels like to be Mary Michael's eighty-three-year-old mother.

I have this vision problem called left-side neglect. That means that while my eyesight is perfectly fine, a portion of it simply doesn't register on the brain. To fight this, therapists do things like place items I need on the left side of the table at lunch. This forces me into the habit of looking left whenever I need something. It's not so bad.

I can't whistle, which is one of the few things that really bugs me. How will I ever call my little dog, Spike? At least my lips are growing stronger, so I'm mortified less often when food drops from my mouth and onto the table or, worse, someone else's plate.

I also have cognitive problems. Organization problems. Perception problems. And memory problems.

I am unable to form new memories, so I can never say what I had for lunch or breakfast, or if today is Tuesday or Friday, the day my family is due to visit (I am forever wheeling down to the elevators in anticipation).

Old memories are not disturbed. Maybe it's because I can't form new memories that the old ones now haunt me. The other day, for example, one of my young friends here, a proud new papa, was released for the weekend to attend his son's christening. This triggered off a memory about my old Yankee grandma, which I then used as the basis for a homework writing assignment in cognitive therapy.

Jane, the cognitive therapist, seems intent on getting my writing shifts in gear *pronto*. Here, edited only for context and confused imagery, is my first post-hemorrhage attempt at writing something other than a journal entry. It isn't so much a story as an evocation of humble, working-class beginnings, a "Remembrance of Things Past" that might be filled with longing for plain blue-collar bagels instead of dainty upper-crust madeleines. Yet it introduces a life full of colorful characters, events, and themes while demonstrating the brain's miraculous ability to perform on one level while, on so many others, it appears to be in a holding pattern, waiting for some opportunity to once again become whole.

I, myself, am honestly amazed by a broken brain's use of acceptable vocabulary and by the amusing references to a nun from third grade who was not, certainly, as amusing to that small child as she seems now, some forty years later. This is what I wrote:

I Baptize Thee, Grandma, in the Name of the Father, and of the Son, and of the Holy Spirit, Nee Ghost

While we now say *Holy Spirit,* a term far more fitting and respectful than *Holy Ghost,* a name that never failed to remind me of a childhood cartoon character named Casper, I use the word

Ghost here because I'm writing about the 1950s, and in the 1950s that's what He was.

The story, such as it is, belonged to a grandmother who sometimes insisted she was of Irish extraction, sometimes German, sometimes old Dutch with a little American Indian thrown in. Sometimes she would chuck it all and insist she was "a true Yank." Her name was Stine.

True Yank is what I settled on, and her dialect seemed to confirm this: *chimney,* for example, was "chimbley," and *faucet* was "facet," and not for a second could a final *r* be found in her vocabulary. I, therefore, was "Peedah"; she was my "grandmothuh."

Sometimes she would tell this little story on a hot summer night as we caught the breezes from passing cars while sitting on "Grandma's stoop," an open-sided structure with steps, attached to her two-family flat. There we would sit, grown-ups on chairs, kids on steps, licking a "toot," or ice-cream cone, which Old Lady MacManus or Sissy Skiffington might have "blown," or treated, us to from Al's candy store across "the tracks," or avenue, where the Long Island Railroad had run its main line for many years before going subterranean.

Or, we might have heard her story during the ravages of those 1940s winters when we'd huddle all bundled and cozy next to Grandma's antiquated potbellied stove, the wind howling down the "chimbley" or banging at the front door, a frightening noise that Grandma would explain away as the poor souls in purgatory knocking for our prayers. My sister, Patricia, and I would fall immediately to our knees with a few quick Our Fathers and Hail Marys, with maybe a Glory Be or two thrown in. Then Grandma would tell us the little story of how I baptized her.

Or, we all might force it out of her at some family gathering, like spaghetti night at Aunt Anna's, say, when we wanted Grandma in the spotlight because we loved her so and because she would make us laugh so. On these occasions, some now-deceased aunt or uncle would invariably pipe up with: "Okay, Grandma, now tell us how Peter baptized you."

And here is the story, such as it is:

Mine had been a difficult delivery, as had been that of my sister a few years earlier. Accordingly, the doctor ordered my mother hospitalized for a full eleven days, which, for the 1940s, was really not unusual. I'd give you the exact date of this tale, the day I was brought home from the hospital, but math has never exactly been my forte, a simple fact that haunted me through every long division problem that Sister Attila Marie tried teaching me in third grade via her famous, usually foolproof, hair-tugging method. (Her name was not Attila, of course. We simply called her that because of her Hun-like traits and because we loved referring to her as "Attila the Nun.") Note that while Sister Attila Marie's hair-tugging method was notoriously effective with years, if not generations, of my predecessors, it was a total bomb with yours truly, placing me in the unenviable position of being the only third-grader at St. Elizabeth's Parochial with a bald patch where every other boy had a cowlick.

If you complained, she might threaten to have the issue settled by your parents, a mortal embarrassment. Mostly, though, she would toss off the whole situation with a flip little aphorism like, "Hair today, gone tomorrow."

She was forever saying things like that as well as stuff like, "Too many cooks spoil the broth" and "He who lives in a glass house should not throw stones" and "A stitch in time saves nine."

A regular Ben Franklin.

And now to attempt my math problem, which is to add the eleven days of my mother's hospital stay to my date of birth, September 25:

Okay, I've got it.

October 5.

Right?

Tell you what. If I'm wrong, I'll run across the tracks and blow you to a toot. Fair enough?

So anyway: "Come on, tell us, Grandma, how did Peter baptize you?"

"I was helping Alice [my mother] get ready to leave the hospital," she would begin to a roomful of relatives already sniggering in anticipation of the belly laugh to come, "and she asked me to change the baby's diaper.

"Well, I had nine [babies] myself, of course, so I could do this backward, blindfolded, and in fourteen languages," she would add colorfully. Grandma was one colorful old lady.

"Colorful is as colorful does," Attila the Nun would have said, I'll bet you.

"But I didn't cover the baby up proper," Grandma'd continue, "and so when I leaned over to get a safety pin, *whoosh* comes this geyser straight into the air like a yellow Old Faithful, except with my face in the middle of it!" With this she would trace an imaginary jettison from an imaginary baby's changing table to her very real, mugging face.

Note to Jane: This was an admittedly tiny, admittedly banal little story, yet my grandmother would tell it with such sweetness and such naiveté that by the time she would pretend to mop the pretend offense from her real, mugging face, the entire room would be collapsed into helpless, howling laughter.

Well, it's no *GWTW,* maybe, but that's the story.

Grandma was so sweet, so free of malice, so downright innocent, you would have laughed too, believe me.

Well, the thing that made it funny, see, was her facial expression, which you really had to see; and that funny, gruff voice, like the lady in those old "Where's the beef?" commercials, a voice you really had to hear because without it, "Where's the beef?" really isn't very funny at all.

Okay, Jane, okay. You had to be there.

* * *

May 29, 1992. Another day in this not-so-typical joint. The reason I say it is not so typical is that, first, it really doesn't seem like a hospital. More like a pleasant housing complex, say, or maybe an elite kind of school that most of us could not afford. So much like a school that I have, in fact, developed the cloying habit, when leaving people, of saying, "See you around the campus."

Blame it on my condition. (Secretly, I sometimes wonder if, without knowing it, I have been committed to the booby hatch.)

As usual, I pretend to be progressing by leaps and bounds, though I am not. My left hand could not move if my life depended on it, and I can't kick this funny image that it is a transplant from some other guy who actually died around March or April. It is not atrophied or rotted or anything like that. It is just totally useless and it ticks me off how this useless appendage just hangs here contributing nothing whatsoever toward its keep. Nevertheless, I remain all smiles, all confidence, all hope. A lot of this is insincere. I determined on the very first day I was here, see, that I would be the kind of person who always finds the glass half full, if you know what I mean. When someone says, "Hi, how are you?" I never simply say, "Fine, thank you." Oh, no. What I say is this:

"A little better every day, thanks."

I am downright disgusting.

But I do believe that attitude is everything. I do believe that just as my brain broke down, it can be taught to run on all cylinders again. And I do believe in God, which is really something for a declared atheist.

One of the many reasons I now believe in God is that I really shouldn't be here, alive and writing, yet here I am.

If I did live, the medics told my darling, frightened wife, it was with the possibility of being effectively brain dead.

I have thought about this long and hard and have decided that if I had become what is so affectionately known in the medical trade as a "human vegetable" I would want to be broccoli. This will give you some idea of my defiant, hateful attitude toward our current (in 1992) chief executive, Mr. George Bush. Another vegetable I might pick is kohlrabi. Not because it has a terrific taste, but because it is a terrific word. Just let that roll on your tongue for a minute. *Kohlrabi.* Or here's another one:

Rutabaga.

Can't you just see it?

"Yes sir, ladies and gents. Step right up. For fifty cents, four measly bits, that's five-tenths of one American dollar, you can walk into the tent and cast your peepers on the world's only living creature that is half man, half kohlrabi."

Next week: the Rutabaga Lady.

But like the word or not, I am not a kohlrabi, nor am I any other veggie. My fingers don't ever resemble parsnips, like those of the old men in canvas shoes and straw fedoras hanging out in Al Peretta's barbershop when I was a kid. There they would sit talking of Harry Truman while thumbing through model railroad magazines, the enjoyment of which may be why they so faithfully chose Mr. Peretta. I know that's why I went to him. That and his twenty-gallon tropical fish tank full of neon tetras. Another feature that tickled me back in 1951 or so was that Mr. Peretta played the violin, and I often arrived for my fifty-cent cut to find him regaling the entire neighborhood with "Fascination," say, or "Petticoats of Portugal," or his medley of Puccini highlights.

"Well, well, Peter," I can still hear him say as he sat me in the bumper seat that would make me tall enough for him to reach. "What on earth is happening with this bald spot where a cowlick should be? It never seems to want to grow in."

"That's only because I can't do nine into forty-two," I wanted to tell him, but I was too mortified.

Even now I find my brain muffled in a protective blanket when I even *think* about doing long division. And at forty-nine, I'm too old to learn. I am an old man, remember, or at least feel like one ever since my head exploded last March. Technically speaking, of course, that was not an explosion but an implosion, like a dying star that caves in on itself, causing massive damage. And like a dying star, my own particular supernova ended in what feels like a black hole, sucking in the reality surrounding it, only to spit it back again God knows where and as God knows what.

That's sort of how it feels to be nuts. And let me add that if you're truly nuts, you'll definitely be the last person to know. Everyone walks on eggs around you, but then one day, *wham!* It'll hit you smack in the face. I discovered this for myself the day I could not find the shower room.

I knew it was down the hall and left, toward the end. But one morning I also knew it was down the hall and right, on the way to the nurses' station. I told this to one of my therapists, who said she'd help me so this wouldn't happen again.

Next morning I woke up and wheeled out into the hallway with my towel and shaving gear to see a sign with an arrow pointing to the left. It said:

***Peter:* Shower This Way!**

And there were about six more signs leading to the shower room door, which was plastered with more signs giving variations of:

***Peter:* This Is the Shower!**

Oh, man, you want to talk about embarrassing? The signs may as well have read:

***Shithead:* Shower This Way!**

and:

***Shithead:* This Is the Shower!**

I'm telling you, I felt like the shithead of the decade. This is when I realized, though, that I could be crackers without knowing it. I mean, I'd lost control of my left arm and leg; I'd lost control of my lips so that mealtime became slobber time. Why not just have lost it all and be assigned more or less permanently to the cracker bin?

The hospital, outstanding though it is, is full of patients who, I could most easily be convinced, are all newly hatched from the Cuckoo's Nest. This is because all of us in the TBI unit are brain damaged to some extent. The initials say it all. TBI: Traumatic Brain Injury.

Recent patients at Gaylord have included the Central Park Jogger, whose brain was damaged during the famous *Clockwork Orange*–like attack that nearly took her life and added the word *wilding* to the American vocabulary, increasingly in need of descriptive terms to cover our growing appetite for violence.

Another recent patient here was the son of TV talk show

host Sally Jesse Raphael, who was injured in a traffic accident. I think.

And then there's me.

I feel like a nutcase in my TBI unit. One of the reasons for this is the presence of Charlie the Baker.

Charlie suffered a heart attack but was not given oxygen in time, so his brain became damaged. Another few seconds and he, too, could have entered my sideshow as the Human Eggplant, maybe, or one of the Great Zucchinis.

Charlie, a kind and thoughtful man in his early fifties, remains convinced that this is not a hospital at all, but a commercial bakery that he bought for his parents. He, himself, is the supervisor of the deliverymen, who include me and all the other male patients. Charlie is forever running over our duties with us, forever asking if all the trucks are in working order, if all the men have punched in, if it's time to wash the trucks, stuff like that. Charlie is kind and considerate, well liked by all, the kind of fellow I would like to know if we're ever both well. I hope he is well soon. He is in my prayers.

I took it upon myself to sit Charlie down one beautiful summer afternoon not long ago to explain to him that this is not a bakery but a hospital, and that the men on our floor are not deliverymen but his fellow patients.

"This is a hospital?" he said. "Really? God, it seems so strange. . . . I've had everything f___ed up, haven't I?"

Banzai! I thought as I saw the wattage increase ever so slightly in his mental chandelier. *I've got him!* I was totally convinced that my own approach had worked where all others had failed.

Charlie ruminated overnight on my little truth and beauty session, then sat *me* down the next day.

"I've been thinking about everything you told me," he said, "and you're right. This joint does look like a damned hospital.

That's why, as a present to Mom and Dad, I've decided to have the entire place redone. And listen," he said, urging me close with a crook of the finger, "I want your total input before that first nail is slammed. You're such a nice guy." In a voice laden with appreciation and emotion, he added, "I just want you to know that I'll make damned sure you get anything you want in the new order of things around here.

"Tell me what you want," he said. "You just name it."

So am I nuts? This is a very real worry. Will I ever get home to my Mary Michael and to my Matthew and to my Emily Kate? Will I ever get my life back? Or will I forever remain here, saying, "See you around campus," and being asked if I washed a bakery truck that doesn't exist and feeling like a kohlrabi?

Charlie, as likable as he is, is the guy who does all that yelling. He starts before dawn, and it seems as if he goes through every name in the book.

"Susie!" he'll yell out, or "Debbie!" soon adding more names, exclusively female. Sometimes the name he yells out is this:

"Mother!"

This always makes me think of those very old black-and-white kiddie cartoons where the spider, after causing mayhem for one and all, finally gets it in the end, usually with a knife, and as the black blood spurts, he gasps and says:

"Mudder."

He then plops over on his back and thrusts all eight well-shod feet into the air, gives a death shudder, and croaks.

The thing about Charlie, though, is that strictly speaking he does not yell these names. He drones them. Endlessly. From one hour or so before dawn until around eight o'clock, when it's time to get up, greet the newly risen sun, then go out to the hallway and face the signs that say:

***Shithead:* Shower This Way!**

and:

***Shithead:* This Is the Shower!**

So am I nuts? Will I or any of us here ever really know? Will Mary Michael ever tell me? Or is she, too, part of some conspiracy to keep me locked up forever?

Hey, wait a minute. I wonder, could Mary Michael have told the powers that be about my visit with the Holy Spirit, nee Ghost? I'll tell you, man, if anything would keep me in here forever, that would.

It happened some time ago, during my coma, and it changed my life completely. Frankly, I'm anxious to tell you about it, but the time isn't right. I'm a little nervous about it, and I want everything to come out just right when I do tell you. It's important to me that you understand. It's the kind of thing that could change your life too. So when I am ready, you'll be the first to know. That's a promise.

I just hope you believe me when I do tell you. "Come on, man. I mean, your old Grandma, that's one thing. But the Holy Spirit, nee Ghost? You been at the glue or something?"

* * *

Another person whose presence makes me wonder if my gears are slipping is the Boy with a Head the Size of Cambodia.

I have been in this place long enough to be considered an old-timer. I have adopted the philosophical attitude of an observer, watching people arrive and knowing what's in store for them while they don't. I wonder about Hadjo, which is the nearest my Western ears can come to the name of the young boy who arrived recently. I do not know his story, but I do know that he is Cambodian, an easy guess because of the T-shirt bearing a map of Cambodia, which he constantly wears. This gives me a funny image that I cannot kick. In it, Hadjo bicycles peacefully through a lovely countryside pockmarked by American bomb-holes and with only the scrubbiest hope of new vegetation in a land that, within my own living memory, was ripped to shreds by a nasty little substance called Agent Orange.

In my vision, Hadjo becomes confused by all the bomb-caused changes in this once-familiar terrain. He pulls the bike over to check the map on his shirt, the map that is almost exactly the size of his head. Hadjo seems to be around thirty years old, which would have made him an infant or, as is more likely, prenatal when we Americans were busy making his country both safe for democracy and unfit for human habitation. Now, I don't know much about Agent Orange, but I do know that a lot of people, our own boys included, lost a lot more than their foliage because of it. And I can't help wondering if it had anything to do with the tremendous size of Our Boy Hadjo's head. It is the biggest head I have ever seen, and I immediately sympathize not just with Our Boy Hadjo, but also with the undoubtedly poor, undoubtedly tiny mother whose birth canal was undoubtedly torn asunder by the passage of this enormous head, which is the size of the large Cambodia on his T-shirt.

Poor kid. He's only about nineteen, I just learned. He only looks thirty. For his own mental health, I hope his attitude is this: that he wonders each and every day why we Americans, unlike him, are born with such tiny heads. What will he think of us when he learns that we even have a leader with a private agenda to eliminate broccoli from the face of the earth?

And what will he think of me when he finds out I am actually part Polish, part Swedish, part Dutch, part Native American, and part kohlrabi?

* * *

May 30, 1992. Dawn. Damn him. Charlie. Lousy rat started in an hour ago. Now I can't sleep and there's no one to put coffee on so I can't even wake up enough to write this entry. I am goddam sick of this joint, Memorial Day or no Memorial Day. At least I'll be home for a weekend soon, for Matt's high school graduation on June 14. Get me out of here!

Later: Mom and Dad are here today, Dad puffing like a bull as he pushed my wheelchair up and down the many hills of these beautiful grounds. Mary had a major client meeting and so, for the first time since I became ill, couldn't be here for the weekend. That's okay. Despite the three-hour trip and the thirty-dollar ferry fare, she's been here every weekend and she calls early every morning and every night just before bed. I told her this morning that I was transferred to another building in the middle of last night.

"You wasn't in no other building," Dad said when I repeated this to him. "You're in 227, just like you been since you got here."

I also told Dad about the note I found in my so-called Memory Book, the loose-leaf binder each patient has, in which we keep important reminders for the day. Odd that it is called a Memory Book, since it is the one item that almost every patient consistently forgets.

This is my note:

Don—

They're keeping me prisoner here. I don't know why. Room 1823, I think. Just come up to 18. Shout my name and I'll yell till you find me.

The note was written at Stony Brook University Hospital, the hospital where I had brain surgery before being transferred to Gaylord. Someone had made reference to some cop on the grounds, which is apparently what led me to plot my escape. The only cop I know is named Don, which is how I came up with the name. Not that he could have found me. The note was unsigned.

People who are brain damaged can live in quite a peculiar twilight state. I certainly did and maybe still do. At its worst, it is lonely, frightening, disorienting, and thus easy to see why some people make a habit of trying to escape. Now and again an alarm goes off, because someone has broken into some forbidden area. Then come the heavy footfalls of nurses and attendants as they speed past our rooms yelling a person's name. So often what they are yelling as they race by is this:

"Charlie! Charlie, stop! Charlie!"

I complained to Dad about Charlie and about my poor, broken sleep. He carefully told me a long story about my own occasions of calling out in the night. The story had a point, which made me feel frozen in ice:

It's not poor Charlie who keeps yelling and screaming night after night.

And it's not the Boy with a Head the Size of Cambodia.

Nor is it any of the other patients here. Not the Fireman Who Barks Like a Dog or the Kid Who Booby Traps Wheelchairs or the Girl Who Dances the Hemorrhagic Hop.

No, it's not any one of the other poor brain-damaged people here who wakes the entire floor up dawn after dawn by incessantly calling out every name that anyone ever heard of and who whines for his mother and curses like a Mafia don.

No, the person who causes all this upset and discontent is the very last person I could possibly have expected.

It's me.

4

Trouble in Tahiti

The title of this chapter refers to a fairly obscure Bernstein opus that I have never actually heard. I don't even know, frankly, whether it's an opera, ballet, tone poem, or hula. It's simply used here as an expression in the same way we used it as college sophomores: in reference to any situation that may be on the verge of souring. "Uh oh," I can still hear one of those long-ago Ohio classmates groan sympathetically when told of another long-ago Ohio classmate's problems in human anatomy, statistics, or epistemology: "Trouble in Tahiti."

The Tahiti in this instance is Wallingford, Connecticut, location of Gaylord Hospital. Not that there was any real problem with Gaylord. The problem was with me and with the very long process of understanding, accepting, and then beginning to deal with what actually happened to me.

Reality came slowly. Very slowly. Daily life was a yellow-gray murk with everything and everybody moving at half speed against some unseen current; it was like living underwater. And it was hard—almost impossible—to comprehend that something as mind-numbing as a cerebral hemorrhage had happened not to someone else, but to me. Yet here was the evidence, I realized one morning while brushing my hair with a soft baby brush Mary Michael had bought me (my old brush was too harsh against the still-healing surface of my scalp). Just beneath the fuzz of regrowing hair was a purplish blotch—my souvenir from the neurosurgeon who had entered my skull at that site to remove the growing blood clot, which had been in the process of killing me.

Well, what do you know? I had brain surgery! Me! Was my first astonished reaction.

I also recalled the moment I first saw the effects of my surgery. At my request, Mary Michael had propped up my oddly Victorian chaise-chair-bed (a regular wheelchair had not yet been permitted) before a full-length mirror for a complete and unobstructed view of the damage. We were soon laughing, making cracks about my partially shaved head with its long purple blotch and deep, key-shaped cranial "valley" an inch or so above my right brow. Nervousness probably brought on the laughter, but laugh we did. Take this stuff—even a brain hemorrhage—too seriously, and you're sunk.

"I look like a finalist in a Gorbachev look-alike contest," was my opening crack upon checking out the large purple Rorschach on my head. Then came a round of hole-in-the-head jokes, and I commented that the third "hole" (in addition to the two eye sockets) might come in handy in decades to come, when my skull could be used as the perfect organic bowling ball.

But Mary Michael topped me, as she had done so often over our two-plus decades together. "Just think," she said. "Now we have a perfect place to hide that spare key when we go out."

This sent us into gales of howling laughter, which may have

disturbed the sensibilities of others around us. For me, however, it was my first full understanding that Mary Michael was truly there for me. She completely understood that the only possible way to deal with this catastrophe was to find the humor in it wherever and whenever possible, and that although it might take quite some time—years, in fact—one day I would be fine and able to write and fully contribute support to our lives and those of our kids. Her command to me was loving and simple:

"Think about nothing. Worry about nothing. I will take care of everything—the kids, the bills, the doctors, the insurance, the groceries, the works. You have one job and one job only: get well."

Now, however, deep in thought while using a hairbrush covered with bunnies and duckies, I began to realize that this job of getting well was going to be far more difficult than I had imagined. I was being forced to recognize and accept strange new physical deficits. At the same time, I was suddenly finding myself light-years away from anything like a normal life, living a strict daily routine imposed by strangers, which wasn't helped by my utter inability to comprehend such basic fundamentals as the day of the week. My time perception had been damaged, a common "deficit" among those suffering a traumatic brain injury. In my case, my perception of the day of the week never varied.

It was Friday.

It was always Friday. Friday was the day Mary Michael (often with my parents) would visit me. Mary Michael would then stay the weekend at the nearby Connecticut estate of my beautiful Aunt Florence, but would also spend most of her weekends with me. Mary Michael usually discouraged Matt and Emily Kate from making the long weekend trip, feeling that at their respective ages of eighteen and fifteen, and considering they'd already lived through their father's horrendous depression, they'd seen enough problems and should be free to lead their young lives as normally as possible. I agreed.

The specialized Gaylord routine was designed to guarantee recovery from brain damage as rapidly as possible while keeping each day so structured and busy that a patient would not have an opportunity to fall into the awful pit of depression, a major peril for the newly impaired.

My own habit was to awaken around dawn and call the nurse via intercom to come loosen my bed straps so I could get up. The idea of being bound to one's bed reminded me of some personals ad from the "Kinky Fun" section of *Screw Magazine,* except that in reality, it was neither kinky nor fun. It was unbearable, really, to be strapped in like that, unable to turn or move, and my whining and wheedling became constant. Finally, the Gaylord Powers agreed to a test. I would be left unbound, but with the firm stricture that I was not, under any circumstances, to so much as think of getting out of bed without calling for help.

Failure came on the first night.

Somehow, the very act of grabbing for a urinal at 3:00 A.M. seems to dam the envisioned flow, at least in my case. And, undoubtedly off aiding someone in far greater need than a man who wanted to pee, the nurses simply didn't answer my annoying paging.

In addition to a full-scale shower room that could be located merely by following a series of embarrassing signs, each patient had a private little water closet with toilet and sink so that—well, of course I could go the bathroom myself. I was forty-nine years old; wasn't I a big boy? All I needed to do was twist my newly unfettered body around so that my right foot would hit the floor first—my right leg being firm and reliable, after all, while my left still seemed to belong to Alyssa, Emily's old foam-filled Cabbage Patch Kid.

Twist around, I instructed myself mentally. *Just stand slowly . . . slowly . . . There. Now lean on the nightstand, and . . . and . . . wait a minute, is that the left arm you're leaning with? Dumbo! Big mistake! You know that arm can't hold you. Hell, you can't even . . . Hey, wait a minute, wait a minute, now . . .*

Ker-rash! The nightstand went over in a tornado of swirling bedside effects including lamp, call button, gaily splashing urinal, several pens and pencils, any number of Snickers bars, and, believe it or not, my long-lost Memory Book.

"Hi, Karen," I heard myself saying rather sheepishly to the tall figure of the night nurse whose shadow soon fell across the floor and across my prone body.

Karen, a cheerful and supportive nurse, even to an overweening extent, suddenly "morphed" before my eyes into a hellish combination of Nurse Ratchet and Sister Attila Marie.

"See what happens when you don't follow the rules?" she sputtered in frustration, helping me to my feet while checking for damage. "You promised never to get out of bed! *Never,* under any circumstances!" Sweet little Nurse Karen was so ticked, she even piled on the guilt.

"And you know who would have been blamed if you got hurt? Not you, but me. Me, that's right. *Me!*"

She eventually simmered down, and the incident seemed forgotten with my promise never to let it happen again. Ever.

On the next morning, however, when Georgette, my little Viennese laser beam of an attendant, came for me at the dayroom, she did not wheel me off to my rounds of therapy. Instead, I was whizzed back to my room where a new bed, immediately dubbed "the cage" had been installed. Standing next to it was John, the male nurse who had seen me through one of my most hellish nights. He said that my "self-control problem" had been discussed in that morning's staff meeting, and I was being given the following choice for my own safety: either return to being strapped into bed at night or sleep in the bed he had just rolled in. It was not really a cage, of course; it just seemed like one because it was entirely encased in a "fence" of cord in the design of common chicken wire. One passed into or out of the bed by means of a zipper operated from the exterior only. If I chose this new contraption of a bed, John explained, a call button would be placed inside so that I could still summon help or converse with the night staff via intercom.

"Let me know what you decide," he said as he started out.

"Don't go, John," I cried out, "the choice is clear. I'll take the cage." I would have preferred anything over being bound and trussed like a Christmas goose. The only things missing were a chestnut stuffing and a nice cherry glaze.

* * *

When Mary Michael called every morning at seven o'clock, she would hear all my fears of the night: how I'd been secretly transported to another building, how I'd spent the night in the hospital's "death room" to await "the inevitable," or, most persistent, how someone had again screamed through the night because the "doctors" here had ripped out his liver without the benefit of anesthesia. Was I next? Was that what was intended when you were taken in your sleep to another building and the death room? Why was I there? And what was Mary Michael doing to get me the hell out? Mary Michael would whisper calming, motherly assurances and then have me look around my room as she described its color, shape, and furnishings; the location of the bathroom, the TV, and the entrance. She would repeat this with infinite patience until I would finally accept that all was indeed okay; she'd then say good-bye with a promise to call back at bedtime. Our morning call completed, the day of activities could begin.

At eight o'clock came breakfast, usually taken in my room.

Then came one of the day's few unstructured moments, a time most patients used for personal business and assignments from cognitive therapy. I used the time to wheel down to the elevators since I believed it was Friday and I had to wait for my wife and family. Eventually, the staff caught on and I would be urged back to my room, using the remaining time to write in my journal or to attempt calls home. The operative word here is *attempt,* since I couldn't divine how one got a line. At last, dear Dad gave me all the toll booth quarters saved up in his car so I could dial directly from the pay phone in the hall. Yet even this brought problems. Just listen to one stranger who'd had it with my dialing errors:

"Look, Mister," he yelled after my repeated calls, "I don't know who you are or what you want. But there ain't no Mary Michael here! And there ain't no Matt and no Emily and no Mom and no Dad. So knock this off and go get a life or go get yourself checked into Bellevue or whatever, just leave me alone, *kabeesh?*" The force of his slamming phone was so powerful that I could imagine wires being knocked off utility poles from his house to Gaylord. I soon became too discouraged to attempt talking sense into this man or the many others I'd inadvertently reached, so I used Dad's quarters for Snickers bars and waited silently for Georgette, whose job it was to whoosh all 215 pounds of me to various therapies and to keep tabs on me for the day.

First came occupational therapy, where the primary therapist, Carolyn, performed the painful necessity of "ranging," or stretching, my motionless left arm, an unbendable 4 x 4 newel glued to my shoulder. One could sense (and sometimes hear) the creaking of that shoulder joint as Carolyn worked away, determined that it would one day move again at my command, not hers. Then came the bending of my elbow, more like the bending of a kindling branch at that moment just before it cracks in two. Next came my wrist, surrendering in groaning protest like a palm tree in a hurricane, and then my fingers, the little bundle of twigs that had been unmovable since that morning on the phone with Mike.

The next stop on the daily therapy trek was the gym and physical therapy with Judy: an hour of calisthenics during which, among many other exercises, we patients would be taken from our wheelchairs so we could practice walking back and forth along rail-protected rampways. I became part of a team of three men who would also be taken outside to shoot one-handed baskets, whack a badminton birdie, or toss a Nerf ball around our little circle of wheelchairs. It felt like high school and a patient named Ernie, in particular, would often pull high school stunts like arriving late for what he called "gym class" or hiding snacks near the basketball courts. He called Judy "teacher," talked about how best to avoid demerits, and on one occasion even mentioned the possibility of getting detention.

Ernie was a sturdy, well-built guy in his forties who, before his brain injury, had imposed upon himself the lifestyle of a far younger man. He was a victim of what my wife and her 1970s fem-lib friends had called the "Peter Pan Complex," the affliction of middle-aged men who deny approaching age by aligning themselves with far younger women and by living in a manner more appropriate to that younger age group.

Ernie had left his first wife a couple of years earlier and was now married to a woman in her early twenties. He talked often and at length about how he missed "boffing" her and couldn't wait to get out of this joint so he could "boff till the cows come home." He had many "toys" better suited to a more youthful man and had, in fact, received his TBI after being thrown from one of those toys—a motorcycle—in one of those states that foolishly resists a helmet law.

The amazing thing about Ernie was that, while he couldn't

walk very well, and while he ate too much junk food, which he kept hidden around the property, and while he had this Peter Pan Complex and got under everybody's skin by talking about boffing all the time and by relating everything we did to high school, all was forgiven the moment he was handed a basketball and rolled his wheelchair to the foul line. You could almost hear a dramatic roll of drums as Ernie would just sit there in his chair, eye on the goal. Then he would balance the ball in one hand like Meadowlark Lemon while he got a bead on the basket, slowly giving the catapult-hand a test try or two before letting it loose. Then a sly little smile would cross ol' Ernie's face and off the ball would fly, making its perfectly gauged arc until *whoosh!* Two points! Every time! Without fail! Ever!

The third man in our little sporting circle was Jim, a Methodist minister from Brooklyn who was referred to as "Father" by Ernie despite Jim's frequent reminders that he was a minister, not a Catholic priest. Ernie told me Father Jim's story one day while waiting for our ride to swimming therapy at the Waterbury YWCA.

Father Jim was also an English teacher, according to Ernie, with a hang-up about incorrect grammar used in public places, particularly regarding the possessive.

"Like it would drive him nuts," Ernie said, if you would visit the Johnsons, let's say, and the sign on their house read, "The Johnson's" instead of "The Johnsons."

At the time, the story goes, there was a graffiti artist roaming the New York subways writing the same graffito again and again on doors, walls, and car cards:

"Jesus, I love you. Save soul's."

Father Jim, according to Ernie, would roam the subway cars armed with a grease crayon, making the following proofreader's correction to each and every graffito, changing:

"Jesus, I love you. Save soul's."

to:

"Jesus, I love you. Save souls."

One day, while on his secret mission, Father Jim, a slight man now getting on in years, became lost in the labyrinth of filthy, deserted gray tunnels beneath Penn Station in Manhattan. Alone and frightened, he was spotted by a gang of teenage thugs, who called him names and soon gave chase. The situation seemed hopeless for Father Jim, since the tunnels (which are all twisted and connected) invariably led back to one punk or another. At last he saw a clear path to a stairway. Lunging up the stairs, he came to a stranger waiting at the top. Unfortunately, this was no stranger, either, but another one of the young hoods. Jim started yelling. The hood whacked him on the head with the butt of his revolver. Jimmy did not black out for a few minutes and then simply come to, as Hollywood and virtually all of crime literature would have us believe. Instead, he went into a coma for several weeks. When he awoke, it wasn't just his wallet that was missing—he'd also lost a great deal of his basic intelligence and the use of the entire left side of his body.

Just before lunch it was back to occupational therapy for ADL, activities of daily living. This therapy helps newly impaired people adjust to the world around them, teaching them to put on socks and shoes with one hand, for example, or to button their buttons, butter their toast without the bread sliding off the counter, and, well, you get the idea. A special feature was the privilege each of us had to plan and prepare lunch for our group. When Ernie's turn came, he planned soup and sandwiches. When Jim's turn came, he planned soup and sandwiches. When my turn came, I planned cream of tomato soup, then steamed mussels with crusty sourdough bread followed by Key lime pie.

We had soup and sandwiches.

It was also my fate to be placed with Jim and Ernie for our regular lunch. We ate in the dayroom, which, aside from tables and chairs to accommodate all twenty or thirty souls in our unit, contained sofas and club chairs, the usual number of outdated magazines, and a large TV. On one wall was a changeable sign that announced the day of the week. Knowing the day was never a problem for me, of course.

It was Friday.

Also at our table was Gertrude, the Mother of All Mothers, who seemed forever to be clucking over the rest of us, solving all of life's little problems.

"Now, Jim, be careful with that salt; you want to watch your sodium," she might say, or, "Peter, you didn't get your dessert? Here, let me get you some." She was also terribly protective, cautioning others to say nothing, for example, when food fell from the left side of my mouth, as it sometimes did for several months. Gert's concern reached into every aspect of Gaylord life: Was Jim's pillow too soft? She'd talk to the girl and order up another. Was Ernie having trouble with the calls from his wife? She'd have the lines checked. Was Hadjo not eating properly? Time for a lecture on the importance of eating to get well, whether you liked Western foods or not. (The food at Gaylord was especially good. She let Hadjo know that too.)

Gert also served as gossip central; she knew the story behind the story on everyone, including the good-looking young redhead dubbed the Girl Who Dances the Hemorrhagic Hop. Her real name was Gina and her brain was "fried," according to Gert, from drug abuse. Gina did remind us of Jim, the Christopher Lloyd character on the TV series *Taxi,* whose brain had also been fried via drug abuse. The difference here, of course, was that Gina was a real, not an invented, character, and her relatively tender age of twenty made her situation very sad, indeed.

At any given time, Gina could be found standing rigid, endlessly shifting her weight from one leg to the other. This rhythmic bounce gave birth to the term *Hemorrhagic Hop,* and Gina became a source of endless concern for Gertrude, who was forever involving herself with the time and length of Gina's parental visits, as well as with information regarding the welfare and whereabouts of her siblings and extended family. She worried about how well Gina was sleeping and eating, whether she was cooperating with her therapists or cursing them out like "a truck-stop whore," as she'd so often done, and whether her welfare, in general, was seen to.

Gertrude was a positive, welcome force within our unit. But one day, when I wandered accidentally into her room, there was Trouble in Tahiti.

People suffering from a traumatic brain injury often have difficulty socializing and may even be a danger to others. They must, therefore, be given private rooms. A special difficulty for me, however, was recognizing my own room, although by now I had memorized its color and could tell you on which side of the window the bathroom was located, where the desk and phone were, and so on.

Gert's room couldn't have looked less like my own. It was another color, a different shape, and was even on the other side of the hall. Yet that's where I ended up one day after therapies, when I'd left my room for another failed attempt at using the pay phone. I knew something was odd about the space but couldn't quite figure out what, and as I approached Gert's nightstand to look for familiar objects, I heard a noise and turned around. Gert!

At that moment I knew, of course, what I had done. But as I turned my chair to her with a smile, apology at the ready, Gert did the very last thing I could have imagined.

She screamed.

And screamed. On and on she went, in a bloodcurdling, eye-popping, most unmotherly shriek that could be heard up and down the halls and even, it seemed, on neighboring floors. Mostly, it was a pure, flat-out scream, but mixed up in there were a few phrases like "What are you doing in my room?" and "Help!" and "Nurse!" and a lot of "Get out! Get out! Get out!" This experience created two major changes for me at Gaylord.

One was another "sign" situation. I could no longer mistake another room for my own. Mine was the one that now had an immodestly large block-lettered sign declaring, what else?

Peter's Room

This, of course, added further injury to an ego already bruised by:

***Shithead:* Shower This Way!**

and:

***Shithead:* This Is the Shower!**

However, it helped a great deal to realize that mine was not the only crime of breaking and entering. For up and down the hall, numerous rooms had signs taped over their doorways:

Charlie's Room

and:

Gina's Room

and:

Ernie's Room

Never once, though, in four-and-a-half months of hospitalization, did I ever see a sign reading

Gertrude's Room

Apparently, Gertrude never, at any time, became confused about which room was hers. A mother knows these things.

The other major change occurred in me, not Gaylord. I desperately wanted my own life back and could not fully understand why I was here. I had to—*had* to—get home.

Trouble in Tahiti.

After lunch came relaxation therapy, taken in the small solarium, an all-glass building appendage jutting out into the lush, peaceful greenery of the surrounding countryside. For those of us who had problems adjusting to our unfamiliar difficulties, relaxation was a key therapy. It was even more important for those, like me, whose problems seemed to have been caused by a blood pressure that had "spiked" violently enough to burst an artery, thereby causing a brain hemorrhage, or hemorrhagic stroke. The basic technique of this therapy was so elementary that I use it to this day in times of stress. Try it:

Close your eyes. Begin a steady, slow rhythm of breathing: in through the nose, out through the mouth. In through the nose, out through the mouth. Now empty your mind. Visualize all the cluttered thoughts pouring out as if from some large pitcher, or picture them leaving through your mouth as you slowly exhale. In through the nose. Out through the mouth. Slowly. Slowly. Now replace all those busy cluttered thoughts with a favorite peaceful image you have preselected. Many would choose a flower garden or a lake or a particularly beautiful walk recalled from childhood. I chose the sea, which I missed so much and with which I was so familiar because of my Long Island home. During these sessions my mind would drift, of course. Following one such occasion I wrote of the place my mind took me to. Here is the result. Note that it's written as if the events described had actually happened. For me, they had.

> Just took a walk with Spike along the ocean. So unbelievably balmy that no hat, no scarf, no gloves were needed. Walking along the surf line where Spike splashed in and out of the spindrift in mock pursuit of gulls and petrels, I began to imagine the tall, broad-shouldered figure of my dad walking with us, still handsome and seeming years younger than his threescore and eleven.
>
> He was saying things about the weather that every child of my generation knows because we've all heard it many times over.
>
> "When I was a kid we had winter!" he said, stopping to wipe sea spray from the thick, heavy glasses that long ago carved a rift into the bridge of his small European nose.
>
> "We had snow from November to April, with drifts piled up to the cajones." I never learned what cajones are, exactly, even after years of both studying Spanish and of dining in Mexican restaurants. I deeply suspect, though, that the reason one will never see "Burritos Cajones" or "Cajones Con Salsa" on a menu is that they are not a specialty dish at all but are more closely related to another of Dad's favorite terms, the "family jewels."
>
> But back to those 1920s winters:
>
> "You was considered lucky if you was still smart enough to have your horse," Dad's shade continued in its Archie Bunker dialect, a detail quite fitting since ol' Arch was

also a Queens, New York, boy, though here the similarity ends. Archie was a bigot. Dad is not.

". . . 'cause a horse was the only way anybody could get around till spring. I remember your Uncle Eddie and your Uncle Freddie, we used to go out and race after the coal wagon down 95th Avenue. We'd carry pails in our hands so when the wagon would hit a crack, bump! comes a piece of coal off the wagon, and we'd throw it into your Aunt Florence's baby carriage to take home."

He paused to heave a sigh. "Things was bad in them days," he continued. "We was just through the Depression and nobody had no money. There was always somebody in the family could use coal, though, so we'd give it to whoever needed it most. Sometimes I'd wait till I got a pailful, then take it as a present to your Grandma Stine when I wanted to see your mother. Some of the boys, they would bring flowers, they would bring chocolates from Al's across the tracks or the Lofts up on the Avenue. Me? I brought a pail of coal." He laughed, looking toward the sun-covered dunes as I whistled for Spike, who had romped into a protected area, about to disturb a nest of piping plovers.

Dad's shade turned back to me, and I remembered how pleasant it always was to hear stories of those long-ago winters.

My body ached to be where my mind was, walking in the cool white Westhampton sand, gazing out to those peacefully rolling waves. Instead, both body and mind were still in relaxation therapy, at some point becoming gently aware of the soft, soothing sound of the New Age music. A great peace would gradually preside. Despite all pain, all anxiety, everything was okay.

Invariably, however, all pastoral bliss would be crudely shattered by the sudden, inexcusably harsh sound of what might have been a chain saw or nearby traffic accident. But it was just someone snoring. Loudly. Gratingly. Gaspingly. Grindingly.

Me.

Relaxation gave way to cognitive therapy, or speech. No one could figure out why it was called speech, especially me, since my brain injury had not affected my speech except for those few initial hemorrhagic moments on the phone with Mike. The session was actually one of cognitive therapy, and the miracle that was performed here was the restoration of the ability to put thoughts together well enough to write once again. We worked on all sorts of elementary math, logic, and reading comprehension problems. We used workbooks and were given assignments by Jane, the cognitive therapist with whom I would often argue, raising my voice or banging my good fist when I could not solve what I knew was some painfully obvious problem. Despite the limited awareness I had at the time, I knew that this was the therapy I needed most if I were ever to write again. This may be why my fury at my own failures sometimes became quite raging; unfortunately, they would sometimes be aimed at poor Jane. The back wall of her office, she pointed out later, was damaged by a ridge I had created by constantly edging my wheelchair back and forth as I strove to complete the various writing tasks she'd assigned. One assignment, since I was a journalist, was to interview Jane, in an attempt to redevelop interviewing techniques. The piece wasn't too bad, but I still cringe at the headline I came up with:

Jane Kosinski, Woman at Work in a Hospital That Works

Sounds like a World War II propaganda film. Makes me wonder how I ever thought I could be a writer.

Another assignment was an imaginary interview with Barbara Bush at the White House in that election year of 1992, using circumstances of my own invention.

My chief invented circumstance was that killer bees had reached as far north as Washington, D.C., and had invaded the White House Rose Garden, site of the interview. Mrs. Bush was reluctant to complain and her husband opposed to ordering the killer bees' extermination.

"Can't lose the ornithologist vote, Babs."

Because so much of the work with Jane was verbal, it was she with whom I could speak most openly. I confided that I was sick of this damned joint and everyone in it, that they had no right keeping me here, that I was going home, that I would find a way, and that there would be no way in hell she or anyone else in this damned place could stop me.

There was Trouble in Tahiti.

* * *

Another problem around this time was my inability to take a proper shower with a dead left arm. Besides being unable to maneuver such simple routines as washing under my right arm, there was a danger of burning the left side of my body, since I still had no feeling there. The solution? Shower with Carolyn! Not every day, just once, for instruction. This was not as traumatic as one might think, due to a daily dose of Lopressor, a powerful blood pressure medication that, aside from making one feel that one's life is being lived underwater, guarantees that a man's sexual interest is roughly equivalent to that of, say, Baby Huey's. Therefore, there is no danger of becoming physically embarrassed by the presence of a woman or anyone else in one's shower.

This led to my personal theory that sex offenders need not (a) submit to castration or (b) have their houses burned down and be driven out of town at midnight by torch- and pitchfork-wielding townsfolk. All they must do is receive the same level of Lopressor given to survivors of brain hemorrhage, and sex simply won't exist. Period. Guaranteed. No problem.

The need to be taught to shower was soon added to my growing list of items that supported the fact that, while I apparently was not a raving lunatic, I had to be mad to some degree, or why was I here? Why was an attendant named Georgette with me for most of my waking hours? Why was I strapped into my wheelchair all day long? Why was it equipped with a magnetic device that would set off an alarm should I attempt to board the elevator or wheel down some forbidden hallway as Charlie the Baker had done so often? Why couldn't I make a simple long-distance call? And why was I kept here, so far from home, surrounded by people who screamed when you came near them or who cursed like a truck-stop whore or who insisted we lived in a bakery or who had a head the size of Cambodia or who made wild animal noises like Eddie, the Fireman Who Barks Like a Dog?

Eddie, who arrived around this time, was a man in his mid-twenties who didn't merely bark like a dog. He made all sorts of animal noises. Growls. Hisses. Howls. Gina said thoughtfully that he might be a werewolf, but I pointed out that that didn't make sense since the noises weren't restricted to a full moon. Gertrude, Mother of All Mothers, would have the story, we knew.

She did.

It seems poor Eddie, recent father to a boy cleverly named Eddie Jr., was a volunteer fireman who, in the process of saving a life during an enormous blaze in a New Hampshire department store, had been forced to jump an interior air shaft where he lost his footing, fell on his head, and bingo! He was a TBI whose brain informed him, at least temporarily, that he was a leopard, maybe, or a puma. His brain also rather thoughtfully provided, however, that he was an ambulatory leopard or puma since, unlike the rest of us, he perambulated with a cane instead of a wheelchair (obviously, a wheelchair can be a real drag when you're out snaring prey for the cubs).

Most of us steered clear of Eddie, not knowing when he might growl or hiss. Or bite. We also steered clear because he seemed to think it pretty damned funny to stick his cane through the spokes of passing wheelchairs, then laugh and laugh (or yap and yap). Still, my chest would never fail to fill with vicarious pride upon passing this young hero's room, and I looked forward to meeting him despite all fears that he might growl, bite, or, even worse, lick my face. Had he saved some osteoporotic dowager cowering in a dark corner, perhaps? Or some helpless child desperately clutching her little Bert or Ernie or, God help us, Barney? His full story was yet to be learned.

The last formal session of the day was group therapy, where, wheelchairs in a circle, we would all get to bitch and complain about how rotten it was to be disabled. The most memorable character in this little circle was the man we all called Willie the Whiner.

Willie never shut up about the pain in his shoulder, the pain in his wrist, the pain in his head, or the pain that went from his shoulder to his wrist to his head. He hated the food, disliked the other patients, found the staff incompetent, despised doing any kind of physical activity (he even circulated a petition for increased nap time), and thought the patient-to-staff ratio wholly unacceptable.

"See this room now?" he asked on one occasion. "Look at us, eight patients, one therapist. What's wrong with this picture?"

Gina stood, shifting weight from one foot to the other as she pondered.

"We got room for more wheelchairs," she said at last.

"We *have* room for more wheelchairs," Father Jim corrected.

"It's snack time!" Ernie said enthusiastically, Gert cautioning that he was eating too much junk food. Charlie asked whether all the trucks were in from their runs. Eddie said nothing for a moment. Then he barked.

"See what I mean?" Willie the Whiner was ticked. "What's this talking supposed to do for us, anyway? We should have more therapists here teaching us how to *do* stuff. You know, paints and watercolors and macramé and woodburning. Not that there's much I can do myself because, well, the pain . . . But no. Here we sit, talking. You want to talk about how it is to be physically impaired, that what you want to talk about? Well, there's no mystery. It stinks, that's all. Two words: It stinks! That what we're supposed to talk about, how much it stinks?"

"Let's talk about that," said the therapist. "In fact, maybe you can elaborate, Willie. We're all interested in your feelings."

"Okay. How about, 'Boy, oh boy, does it ever really and truly honest-to-God stink?'"

The guy was not Little Mary Sunshine.

He was someone who, according to Gert, might do better with a nice, old-fashioned enema.

It was around this point that I was surprised with a terrific taste of home. Since it's been proven that petting a dog or cat can effectively lower blood pressure while presenting an aura of calm and reassurance to both petter and pettee, Mary Michael was encouraged to bring our little dog, Spike, in as a Gaylord visitor. Think of the pup used in Mighty Dog commercials. Now color him yellow and you've got Spike, who, as you can imagine, was a huge hit with everyone at Gaylord. Everyone except Willie, that is, who complained that he was allergic; and Eddie, who resented the challenge to his territory; and Charlie, who was concerned about the rules prohibiting dogs in Connecticut bakeries.

Of the staff, the person most taken with Spike was John, the nurse who had sat up with me during that terror-filled night. John was one of those people who automatically resorts to anthropomorphism in the presence of an animal, especially a cute-as-hell dog like Spike.

"Here's Daddy," John would say to Spike as I drew near. This reminded me of the young girl at our local veterinarian's office who, when returning Spike from a routine flea bath and dip, would say:

"Okay, here's kid number one." She would then return to bring back our cat, Sam, saying:

"And here's kid number two."

Far worse was the couple who, bringing their dog in, referred to each other as "Grandma" and "Grandpa" because their dog had had a litter of puppies.

Spike's visit backfired in the sense that it only made yearnings for home and the return of normal life that much more painful. My hospitalization was approaching three months. Life as a "deficited" person had lost its novelty and now presented increasing problems. Note that in these PC times we do not say *handicapped* or *impaired*. What once were handicaps or impairments are now *deficits*. And a person does not suffer brain damage nowadays, but an *insult* to the brain. It was difficult to get a bead on these new terms, since they fed into the still-growing notion that I was raving mad and had been locked away in this Connecticut funny farm. Even now it's difficult to describe the dreams, fantasies, mental flashes, and déjà vus that recurred throughout the day and night, but I'll try:

I had a growing memory of having been "somewhere else" in my recent past. Memories and images of this "somewhere else" would come and go quickly at unexpected times: during lunch, say, or physical therapy, or while being pushed to appointments by Georgette.

The images occurred in no order and their very existence became troubling. I could easily recall being in a building that seemed a bit like my own country train station, for example. It was a large building, lined with several alcoves and filled with comfortable-looking furniture. An outstanding feature of this space, whatever it was, was utter peace and calm and the sense that whatever was going to happen to me there would be just fine. Walking through (or was I gliding?), I seemed no longer a physical being, but a spiritual one. To test this I tried passing my hand through a piece of furniture. It passed, though I was aware of the furniture's physical presence. What was I testing, and why? The room was filled with people, as if it were a waiting room of some sort. What were they waiting for? They weren't quite people as you and I know them; they were beings who looked like you and I look, but they were completely filled with light, the way a lamp shade looks when the bulb is on. Where had I been to create this bizarre memory? And why was I suddenly concerned about Dotson Rader, my homosexual writer friend, and the condition of his soul? And what was this sense I had of a "wall" of good feelings that had entered the hospital room during initial recovery? And what was this warmth I had felt when our local parish priest christened my forehead and hands with the oils used in the Last Rites of the Roman Catholic Church? Why did I now accept the existence of God?

I also remembered my Mary Michael seated bedside at some point after waking from my coma. She was not filled with light like the others had been but was bathed in it, as if from some outside source. Why? And why after that had I become so smitten, so filled with love each time she came to visit and with each kindness she would perform? Why did I, an outspoken atheist, remember wandering through that enormous waiting room and beyond calling out for Jesus? Why was it that the possibility of another brain hemorrhage didn't worry me because I felt utterly unafraid of death? Why would I have periodic "flashes" of myself exploring alcoves in the waiting room?

There was another mental flash that occurred often, one in which I was in a darkened space, part of a small group hovering in a circle over what seemed to be the source of all warmth, love, and light. What was going on here, anyway?

I didn't describe any of this to the psychiatrist who checked in periodically; the thoughts and images, I knew, could only further confirm what must be her opinion on my increasing madness.

No, I could talk to no one. And there was no real solution for me except, just possibly, one that had been suggested by Charlie the Baker:

Escape.

5

An Uneasy Walk Down Easy Street

Though not within light-years of its exuberant detail, Gaylord's "Easy Street" sometimes called to mind the set for *Sesame Street* and those warmly paternal feelings I'd had years earlier when, as a writer for that show, my own young children were occasionally permitted to play there. Gaylord's Easy Street had no nest for Big Bird, and there was never an Oscar in its trash can, but there was a grocery store that vaguely resembled Mr. Hooper's Candy Store; a luncheonette complete with counter, stools, and a booth; a bank window; a ten- or twelve-seat movie theatre furnished with movie screen, seats, and a video camera used to tape and observe one's movements and speech; advertisements and billboards to read and understand; traffic lights where one could practice street safety; and much role-playing by staff and patients alike. It was as much an evocation of real, everyday street life as could be mustered in the basement of a rehab hospital for the brain damaged in rural Connecticut.

My only problem with Easy Street was that no matter how hard I tried and how much brain-damaged logic I applied to the old directional skills, I could never find it.

Georgette, whose job it was to push me to all therapies and keep an eye on me throughout the day, occasionally would be instructed to move me only in the directions I ordered, to test me.

"This would be easy if we knew the cross street," I cracked on one occasion. "You know, like Easy and Elm, or Easy between Broadway and Third."

Now, Georgette wasn't a dour person. Not at all. She was, however, so intent on laser-beaming me to my day's appointments that she never had time for my nonsense, even when I tried buttering her up. I might extol my love of Wiener schnitzel, for example, or tell her all about the Viennese almond crescents Mary Michael always made at Christmas. I might mention Strauss or his "Die Fledermaus" as if I knew what I was talking about, or I might even speak longingly about the good old days of Gay Vienna, the Austro-Hungarian Empire, and Queen Victoria's favorite kissing cousins, the Hapsburgs.

Was there no shame left? Why on earth did I care whether or not this sweet Austrian pusher of wheelchairs liked me?

It's not that I was devious. And there was certainly no escape plan afoot at this time. But with the vaguest thought of possibly getting out of this place someday, somehow, I believed it would be good to buy the confidence of as many potential aiders and abettors as possible.

"A friend in need is a friend, indeed," Sister Attila Marie would have written on the board.

Meanwhile, no matter what stretch of human memory and reasoning I applied in directing Georgette to Easy Street, the end result was invariably the same.

I would begin by telling her to wheel me to the elevator. So far, so good. Then she would hit me with her first trick question:

"Up or down?"

I would think this out and then carefully decide.

"Down," I would say.

"Are you sure?"

This, of course, was her second trick question. But I was onto these Hapsburg types, and there was no fooling me, so:

"Yes," I would say with as much cocksureness as could be mustered.

"Are you really sure?"

Uh-oh, was I really sure? Trouble in Tahiti. But:

"Yes," I would say, because I was one heck of a self-assured guy.

"That boy knows his apples," my old Yankee grandma used to say. "There's no fooling him." And so Georgette, taking in my firm, take-no-prisoners, Yankee grandma expression, would ask which floor to push.

"Basement," I would say.

Now would come that "Ach, are you stupid" look she conveyed so well. Still, I would be firm.

I was a boy who knew his apples.

And so down we went to the basement level, location of one of the gyms, a number of private offices, and the boiler room with the little closet next to it that contained a very large slop sink. Along the way, Georgette would pause at every junction to faithfully follow direction orders. Finally we'd come to a stop at the slop-sink door, where I'd confidently led us.

"Is this it?" she would ask. Yet another in the unending stream of trick questions from the Austro-Hungarian Empire.

"Yes," I would quite naturally insist. "Just open the door."

And there I would sit in the yellow-gray basement light, Georgette behind me at the wheelchair controls, both of us facing a huge slop sink loaded with all manner of, well, slop.

Why the space above the sink didn't carry that big electric

sign flashing "Easy Street" was as much an imponderable mystery as what happened to the Memory Book I kept forgetting. Or how to get an outside line. Or how my room had a strange way of becoming other people's rooms. Or why I had so many strange, otherworldly dreams and recollections. Or what day it could be if it wasn't Friday.

As a matter of fact, I couldn't even tell the difference between morning and evening and was kind of ticked at the thrifty guy who, a millennium or two ago, designed clocks to repeat the same numbers each day.

So, because of some economy-minded ancient Roman sundial-making nerd who today would work for Apple or Digital, the luncheonette on Easy Street was often open after midnight, the *Today* show came on at seven o'clock in the evening, and Peter Jennings and Alex Trebeck appeared just when I was on my way to my morning shower. My solution was recorded in a journal entry, heavily edited as per usual.

> *June 1, 1992.* Finally figured what's morning and what's evening. Sun comes up outside my window, so no matter what's on TV, it's morning. No sun on my side? It's evening. Cloudy day? Bite the bullet. Ask. Carolyn (my chief therapist) was so happy with this brilliant solution, she did everything but throw me a testimonial dinner. I'm relieved. At least she won't have to make any more signs.

Carolyn also decided it was time for more extreme measures to reduce the extraordinary rigidity of my left arm, a condition known as "excess tone."

It was this excess tone that caused the top of my left wrist to appear soldered to the bottom of my chin and gave me the oft-mentioned feeling that the arm itself was a transplant from a donor who had not merely died before surgery, but had gone into *rigor mortis severis*.

"All I need is a pocketbook dangling from my wrist, a pair of rosary beads, and a dowager's hump," I told Carolyn, "and I'd look like one of my grandmother's lady friends at morning Mass."

Carolyn tried not to laugh at remarks like this, but understood that since I was usually making light of my own condition and not anyone else's, it was okay.

Besides, she had a tough job to perform, and if I could joke, she could laugh, I told her. Sometimes it was a real problem for Carolyn to daily pry my arm away from my chin in the lengthy, painful process of "stretching" mentioned before. I can still see the look of dread on her sympathetic, pretty face as she tugged and pulled, apologizing and taking a little break each time she heard the tiniest involuntary gasp of pain.

There was also much pain in that shoulder at night, leading me to Tylenol after Tylenol accompanied by the memory of my left leg collapsing months earlier when I walked down the apse of the Sistine after crashing painfully into the kitchen doorway. Carolyn made me understand that it was the increased tone and not the crash that caused my present pain, and that it was her job to help decrease that tone now, though it was a job she detested because, although necessary, the process was so painful.

One morning, seeing her close her eyes at the pain she was inflicting, I jokingly began to do the Lamaze breathing my wife and I had learned years ago when she was pregnant with Matt and then Emily Kate.

"He-he-WHOO! He-he-WHOO! He-he-WHOO!"

Soon Carolyn was choking with laughter, neither one of us aware of pain. I was being the class clown, and I knew it. A regular Jerry Lewis.

"He laughs best who laughs first at himself," Sister Attila Marie would have said, or something complicated like that.

The biggest problem for Carolyn was my fingers. To get an idea of how tight a brain-injured person's fingers can be, try this:

Make a fist. Tight. No, tighter. Tight as you can get it. Really, come on. Okay, that's better. Now, try to "break" that fist with your other hand. Seems impossible, right?

That is what Carolyn had to face every morning. At first, she tried a second stretching session each day, sometimes calling in an associate to help "break" those little flesh-covered cast-iron rods that had once been fingers. But when this proved futile, she recommended a surgical procedure involving the implantation of electrodes beneath the skin of my left hand. Electrical impulses would then force the recalcitrant muscles to move.

"No way," I said. The *RoboCop* look was not for me.

"It doesn't hurt," Carolyn assured. But she was dealing with a boy who knew his apples.

"You don't understand," I said. "I've had this wild fear of electricity ever since the shocks I got from my first Lionel set."

My first Lionel electric train set had been a Christmas gift allegedly from Santa, but in my heart I knew it was previously owned by my older cousin, Frankie, who lived downstairs from us in the two-family house we occupied on Atlantic Avenue in the working-class section of Ozone Park.

We were poor. We didn't know it and my mother still doesn't feel that was true, since we never went hungry. But we never had very much of our own, that's for sure. Mom (whom we called "Mother" as kids) worked as a machine operator at the Metal Etching Corporation, a nearby factory, and our father was a coal delivery man for Old Man Sanatore, then a grave digger at Cypress Hills Cemetery, and numerous other things before he was accepted, with pride and delight, for a permanent maintenance job with New York City's Department of Parks. Mother and Dad both worked exceedingly hard without a complaint, not so much as a "Boy, am I tired." The rent for our cold-water flat was always paid; we had heat in winter; the electricity and gas stayed on; we eventually got our own TV instead of always having to run down to Aunt Anna's for *Children's Hour,* or *The Magic Cottage,* or *Pinky Lee,* or, best of all, Tuesday nights and *The Texaco Star Theatre,* starring Milton Berle. Many years later—I don't know how—my parents saw to it that I was the first kid in my family, or on my block, or that I'd ever heard of, who was sent to college.

And there was always food on the table. Aunt Anna, who lived downstairs, had married Uncle Joe, a good man of Italian descent, and there seemed no end to the spaghetti she might produce. Or the homemade ravioli. Or the Friday-night pasta e fagiolli ("bastafazool"). Aunt Kitty, my father's sister, worked in a bakery, so we were never without bread and goodies. Sometimes we would have a supper consisting entirely of "mush," which was broken-up Uneeda Biscuits sprinkled with sugar and doused with hot milk. We kids loved it, especially the sugar, a suddenly unforbidden treat. And sometimes Grandma Stine would send over a platter of her world-famous browned chicken. It wasn't until years later that we discovered the well-kept secret of her world-famous browned chicken.

She burned it.

This was okay with us.

Christmas never failed to be a time of plenty, especially for me that year. After all, I finally had my clutches on that Lionel set which my cousin Frankie had played with only in their spooky basement, leading everyone to assume I had never seen it, so it would be fine as a gift.

But a boy who knows his apples knows his Lionel sets, and I couldn't have been happier, no matter where it came from.

My only problem was shocks.

Model trains used to (and probably still do) have loads of smack-ups, meaning you're forever setting them back up, touching the tracks as you do. It's not so bad to touch tracks now, but in the fifties, there was a special rail that carried the electricity. This is the rail I seemed always to be touching, usually with some nice piece of metal. The result? Tears of pain and frustration (how could my favorite toy do this to me?) and years of neurotic fear of electricity that persists to this day.

There would be no electrodes buried in this Casey Jones's hand, thank you.

"I promise you, Peter, there are no electric shocks involved," Carolyn claimed again and again. She seemed sincere, all right, and I liked and trusted her. But I was a big baby, so:

"No way," I insisted.

"Okay, then we'll try serial casting first, then come back to this if we have to."

Cornered by both logic and this revelation of my own cowardice, I agreed.

Serial casting, in this case, required placing my entire left arm, from shoulder to knuckles, in a plaster cast. The second stage in the "series," executed a week or two later, involved a smaller cast. The third and final cast involved only the wrist area. Finally, a single, skin-tight Isotoner glove would have to be worn for months, as it turned out, reducing the swelling and the tone while forcing me to endure every Michael Jackson joke conceived by the Western mind.

The casting process is uncomfortable, unwieldy, unmanageable, smelly, sweaty, and itchy. But the alternative of being charged with electricity like Dr. Frankenstein's sidekick kept my lips firmly soldered. I didn't dare complain, not with thoughts of lights dimming throughout Wallingford, Connecticut, and of my hair singeing and eyeballs turning to jelly any time I attempted to move a finger by means of this device.

No matter how itchy, smelly, or hot, the casts were okay by me.

* * *

In addition to its store setting and movie theatre, Easy Street contained a small parklike area with a table and benches, where we sometimes gathered in small groups to go over such assignments as preparing a joke to tell everyone or bringing in newspaper clippings on various topics that might ignite some form of "roundtable" discussion designed to keep us involved in life. Ernie called this activity "Current Events." He brought in sports items. Gertrude brought in recipes and restaurant reviews. Gina got editorials, and Father Jim got religious news. Surprisingly in this election year, nobody wanted politics.

I got politics.

It wasn't a pretty sight, either, being probably the only left-leaning TBI in all of southern Connecticut. In addition, it was especially difficult for TBIs who can't remember the day of the week or where their rooms are to become embroiled in a discussion on even the most compelling political issue, like killer bees in the White House Rose Garden or the elimination of broccoli from the face of the earth.

Easy Street was no *Crossfire,* that's for sure.

Crossfire, of course, was now on at 7:00 A.M., Eastern time, and so I often missed it. This was okay, though, since it was Friday, anyway, and my family was due. One thing I did seem to catch each evening without fail, however, was a long-running commercial for an alarm system. It featured three convincingly snarly actors, dirty, scar-faced, unshaven, and looking as if they'd spent too much time on Devil's Island without a pretty face to slice. They'd take turns describing techniques of breaking and entering homes, the final teaser being, "The houses without alarm systems—they're the ones you go for!"

We didn't have an alarm system at home in Westhampton.

So now, in addition to convincing myself that I was locked away in some funny farm from which I might be forced to escape, and aside from the nightly images flooding my mind about crashing into door frames and passing into unconsciousness, I had a whole new fear that my wife and fifteen-year-old daughter were in the clutches of some potato-faced thug who slits throats from ear to ear as part of a daily workout before putting in his Richard Simmons tape. The thought at last became so obsessive that Joan, the pretty young hospital psychiatrist, was summoned on my behalf.

"Consider what's just happened to you, Peter," she said. "You're only in your forties; you were a bit overweight, you said, but not in bad physical condition; you were not suffering hypertension or any condition known to lead to a stroke, yet it happened.

"One thing you learned from this experience, in fact, is that the impossible can and does happen. But, please, you can't let yourself think that impossible things happen all the time to the same people, because they don't. Your wife and daughter are fine. And don't forget, you've got a pretty big, muscular son there to help look over things at home."

This made tremendous sense, but it didn't help. Each sunset brought stark new terrors of the Visigoths descending from the Carpathians to rape and ravage my women. And even though my "deficits" guaranteed my being of little use should our little Westhampton fortress-by-the-sea be attacked by nail-spitting, throat-slicing renegades from Devil's Island, my place was there with the family: More than ever, I needed to be home!

Instead of being home defending wife and family, however, I was lost in some loony bin trying to remember jokes to bring in to some loopy place called Easy Street for what some oversexed guy named Ernie called "Current Events."

When our "prepare a joke" assignment came due, Gina told a very funny but very filthy joke involving a zucchini (don't ask); Ernie told one about three college professors, one a German, one a Jew, and one a Pole; Gertrude's involved a woman and her two sets of twins; Father Jim told one of those old "moron" jokes; and me? Here's what I dredged up, but not before making the cardinal error in the joke-tellers lexicon: I told everyone that this was one of the funniest jokes I'd ever heard and that they were all going to love it, thus building myself up for a letdown. Here's the joke:

Setting: the Vatican. The pope is seeking to elevate one Italian archbishop to the position of cardinal and is making his final choice, testing the three remaining candidates.

"I will make the final choice," he says, "by seeing who best answers this most important question." He turns to the first.

"Why shoo, you Holiness," the archbishop of Milan answers, "Anything you gonna ask, I gonna do my best. You be happy."

"Very well, my son, here is the question: What is the meaning of Easter?"

"Easter? Hey, that's-a easy, you Holiness. Easter, she's-a the time when you go into the woods, you find a nice tree. You bring in the house, you put tinsel, you put lights, you buy presents, you sing songs. . . ."

"I'm sorry, my son, that is an incorrect answer. Next!"

The pope asks the same question of the archbishop of Trieste.

"Oh, Easter! Yeah, sure, Easter. That's-a when you go out, you shoot youself a nice fat turkey, you make cranberry sauce, sweet potatoes, pumpkin pie. . . ."

"Next!"

The final candidate, the archbishop of Assisi, comes silently forward. He looks up when the pope asks his question, smiles meekly as he lowers his eyes, and answers:

"Easter, Your Holiness? That's-a when Our Lord, Jesus Christ, rises from the dead inside His tomb. He raises His hand and this giant rock in the entry of the tomb rolls back. He steps forward slowly, slowly, out into the gorgeous, sun-filled Easter morning—then, if He sees His shadow, you got-a six more weeks of winter!"

Some people laugh uproariously at this joke. Some laugh more quietly. But always, always, there is a laugh. My reaction on this Easy Street occasion:

Silence.

The silence of the tomb. I looked around at the faces to realize everyone was staring at Father Jim, who looked as if he'd just swallowed all the altar candles, lit.

I had just broken my own first rule about jokes:

Know your audience.

This meant there'd be Trouble in Tahiti.

Not only had I offended Father Jim, see, whose embarrassment and rage were clearly rising on some inner tide, I had also offended Gina, the young redhead of Italian extraction, with my mock accent.

Just when things were on the mend with Gertrude, who had finally stopped screaming each time she saw me, I now had meek and pleasant Father Jim turning away from me, as he would do until the day he left Gaylord, and Gina of the flaming red hair and flamingly foul mouth, who said something very close to:

"You think that's f___ing funny? You think it's f___ing hilarious to make f___ing fun jokes about us f___ing Italians?

Hey, why don't you just call us all a bunch of ginzos? Maybe toss in a couple of Mafia hit men?"

And she vowed never to talk to me again.

Later on, I ran into Charlie, with whom I had grown closer since the day I gave him that suggestion for remodeling the bakery. Now he often gave me compliments on the way I carried out my daily job, the speed and courtesy with which I handled the delivery route, and so on.

When I told Charlie my joke he actually laughed. Good old Charlie.

"You get that from Milton Berle?" he asked. I hadn't, but was amazed that he recalled the story I'd told him about meeting Uncle Miltie. Brain-injured people can and do remember things at times, particularly if what's remembered carries with it a strong emotional impact. Humor, say. Or anger. Or shock. My Milton Berle story arguably carries all three. But you should judge that for yourself, so here goes:

In 1989, I'd gone to Los Angeles to do a profile on Loretta Young for *Parade* magazine. People of my generation recall Loretta Young as a quite beautiful woman of our mothers' generation, a 1940s film star who in the 1950s hosted a weekly dramatic series on Sunday night television. Her signature was a swooping entrance onto her set, characterized by a dazzling spin through the doorway and a dainty trip down two or three steps, all accompanied by big, sweepingly unforgettable theme music.

After the interview, an agent took me to lunch at the Beverly Hills Friars Club. Celebrities came and went. By 2:30 or so, everyone was gone except one group in a far corner. All I could see was a dense cloud of cigar smoke; it would have been impossible to know that human beings were within had there not been several sets of men's legs protruding beneath that billowing, impenetrable cloud. My agent friend, however, knew that this cloud contained Milton Berle, president of the club, and his set of cronies, all of whom spent every free afternoon there swapping old show biz stories over decaffeinated coffee and genuine New York marble pound cake (the Manhattan cheese-cake, while preferred, was too fattening and cholesterol-rich). My friend took me to meet Milton.

Note that I feel completely free to use his first name, since this is what he insisted as he sat me next to himself, inviting me to have a drink. I accepted, but soon switched to the cake and coffee these old-timers were having because it seemed like more fun. Milton drew me closer upon discovering who my Hollywood interview subject was, and the men all began a round of Loretta Young stories. Milton's was the best.

"Now, you know she was famous for her 'cuss box,'" he said. I knew of it because of the thorough research I am always afraid not to do on my subjects. But he explained it for some of the others.

"Young wouldn't stand for any cursing," he said, "and that is kind of hard to remember in Hollywood, so the deal was this: A *damn* means you toss a nickel into the box, a *hell* costs you a dime, and so on up the scale. Well, this helped everyone to remember their manners a little better," my friend Milton continued with a puff of his stogie, "and when they slipped, the results would go to charity. Well," he said, deepening his voice dramatically for the next announcement, "suddenly Robert Mitchum is signed on as co-star."

A round of *whoas* and *uh-ohs* went 'round the table immediately, the implication being that Mitchum was someone you didn't mess with. It was further underscored that the actor was not exactly famous for any decorous use of the mother tongue. He was a fine, admired actor, apparently, but one who was also known for his refusal to put up with anything he regarded as nonsense.

"So on the first day of shooting," Milton continued, "he's introduced to Loretta Young and says politely that he's heard about her little cuss box.

"'Oh yes,' Young says, explaining the rules and how strict she was about them and that they were the same for stagehands and co-stars alike.

"'Okay,' says Mitchum, pulling a ten from his wallet and stuffing it in the box. 'This takes care of me for today. Let's go make a movie!'"

Berle was sensational. On he went with story after story, all of which his cronies had heard hundreds of times. But today he had a new audience—me—and was pulling out all the stops, working me the way he would work a room. I was thrilled and honored to have Uncle Miltie performing just for me. Was it because I was a member of the press?

I don't think so. I think it was because he was a particularly terrific guy enjoying his declining years in a particularly terrific way.

"God bless him," I would have said had I believed in God at the time, but I didn't. The explosion inside my head and all that followed, including my own little interior tent revival, were still some three years off.

I arose and said good-bye to Berle and to the group of men, then headed for the men's room. As I was about to finish up there, who pulled into the urinal right next to me? Milt!

I washed my hands and was pulling the door to leave when I heard Milt say:

"Peter, turn around and look at this."

I followed his instruction, and behold! What did Berle want me to see, but the gigantic genitalia he was holding for my inspection!

Don't get him (or me!) wrong—there was nothing sexual here, not for a moment. My immediate take on this most bizarre

Hollywood moment was that Berle sought, by offering proof to a member of the press, to substantiate the rumors that had been floating about the tremendous size of this particular appendage.

I am here to tell you that the rumors are true. Think stallion. Think bull. Think Guinness. Think Ripley. Me? All I could think was, "What the hell do I say now?" I mean, here was one of the world's most famous entertainers exposing himself just for me in the men's room of the Beverly Hills Friars Club! What does one say?

"Very nice"?

"My, my!"?

"Say, would you mind a quick snapshot for the wife and kids?"

There is almost no way to cover one's shock and embarrassment at such a moment. Yet I had to, and so I thought quickly, remembering that Milton had just been the subject of a *Parade* cover story written by my friend Dotson Rader.

"What *is* this, Milton?" I said at last. "Are you trying to get another cover story?"

We walked together back to the club's lobby where, being an unabashed cornball, I asked for a snap of myself with my Uncle Milton.

"Let's stand near Ruth," he said, still clearly aggrieved by the recent death of his wife. I followed his direction while he summoned a waiter to take a photo of us standing before the portrait of him with his beloved "Ruthie." Here, true to a lifelong format, my penchant for black humor once again won out over any sense of propriety.

I know what she died of, was the first, and coarser, of my two unspoken wisecracks. The second was:

At least she died happy.

CRACK! comes the sound of a steel-edged ruler in my mind

as Sister Attila Marie raps it on the old wooden desk in front of me, stunning me to attention while filling me with shame before all my little classmates.

"Do you know what this is an example of, boys and girls?" she asks. "It is the classic case of an idle mind being what?"

"The devil's workshop," comes the crystalline sound of forty or so seven-year-olds speaking as one.

"All right, Master Swet," she continues (yes, they really used to call boys "Master" in those days and, yes, the classes really were that large). "In addition to your homework tonight, you will write, 'I must learn respect for the dead' one thousand times in your copybook."

Milton has now remarried and I couldn't be happier for him. I would like to meet this kind, gentle, funny, funny man again one day. Meanwhile, the mental picture I have of him standing in grief before the picture of his wife in the lobby of the Beverly Hills Friars Club will remain the most enduring memory I have of him.

Well, all right, then, it's the *second* most enduring memory.

People love my Berle story, and Charlie was no different. Maybe I should have told it instead of the pope joke on Easy Street that morning. At least I'd have had some friends left beyond good old Charlie, who more and more those days seemed to be dreaming up elaborate schemes on how to escape.

6

The Valley of the Snow Leopard

At some point in early June, Father Jim developed a strange new habit. It was not totally unpleasant—not *totally*—but it could be annoying, and it often seemed quite endless.

He began to sing.

Suddenly. Loudly. Continuously. And without warning.

He would sing in the dayroom. He would sing in the hallways. He would sing at the nurses' desk. In the gym. In the shower room. On the lawns. On Easy Street and in the YWCA swimming pool. Almost anywhere and at any time one might be subjected to that reedy, nasally little (but loud) voice singing "Five Foot Two" or "Goodnight, Irene."

Not that he could sing. Oh, no. Imagine Ross Perot crooning "The Indian Love Call" to Betty Boop. Now you've got the idea. On and on Father Jim went, sometimes coaxing Ernie and me to join in. Sometimes we would.

In physical therapy, for example, when a young woman named Susan became assistant to our physical therapist, Judy, Father Jim could not resist singing "If You Knew Susie."

This little TBI sing-along soon accompanied a rhythmic set of exercises known as the "windshield wiper," which I won't bother to describe except to tell you its purpose is to develop muscle, strength, coordination, balance, and timing.

And voice.

Not exactly Stephen Sondheim. But fun. And Susan enjoyed being celebrated, even if by a trio of men whose combined total brain cell loss was certainly in the millions.

Pretty, raven-haired Susan enjoyed this so much, in fact, that she would even pretend not to notice when Ernie would retrieve one of the boxes of Jujubes or Black Crows from some unknown place inside the "Room of Special Purpose," a mysterious little room just off the gym from which bloodcurdling screams would occasionally spill, upsetting the concentration of those of us who were seriously intent upon learning to walk again. Or to use our hands again. Or to speak, talk, and think again. Or to regain balance and coordination.

Or to learn the second verse of "Five Foot Two."

Summer at Gaylord was like nothing else in my, and probably most people's, experience. Who ever heard of a hospital near a country club? A log cabin for conferences in the woods? An outdoor barbecue grill? Separate cottages for family visits? Tennis? Facilities for sailing on Long Island Sound?

Gaylord had begun life as a tubercular sanitarium. While its more lavish-seeming facilities were generally unavailable to those of us with serious deficits, we were encouraged by knowing, if only by their proximity, that somewhere, somehow, people golfed, played tennis, and led what we once had known as a normal life.

As summer wore on, our little platoon of paralytics was even taken swimming and sailing.

Gaylord now has its own indoor swimming pool, but it was still under construction during my stay there, so tightly supervised hydrotherapy sessions took place at the YWCA in nearby Waterbury, Connecticut. Among my fellow patients who rode with me in the special van were two young men, both in their mid-twenties. One was a more cerebral Ivy League type with blond, aquiline Trevor Howard looks, while the other could only be described (even by a fellow male) as crushingly good looking, Gaylord's own Tom Cruise.

The two young men had forged a deep friendship, obviously based on the bond of disability they shared. Like most of us, they were both confined to wheelchairs, they each had lost the use of one side of their bodies, and their thoughts and perceptions were often muddled and confused. What set them apart was that both had also lost their ability to speak well. This was because they had received serious head injuries to the left cerebral cortex, the seat of speech control, while almost everyone else in our group at that particular time had suffered injuries to the right side of the brain. My own speech had suffered, too, you'll recall, in those first moments following that cerebral explosion. Yet my speech problem was only temporary, for in those early moments of a cerebrovascular "event," a clear path of injury is not quite set.

The path had been set, however, for these two young, fine-looking men. Their faces would contort, as if in pain and anger, with every syllable they uttered. Here, try this experiment. Repeat the following sentence, but with your mouth closed:

"Both young men had lost their ability to speak."

Just try it. Get a feeling of what these two young guys went through. Go ahead, while nobody's listening:

"Both young men had lost their ability to speak."

Okay, that's closer. Now try it again, but add some funny little yodeling sounds in your throat, the weirder (and louder), the better:

"Both young men had lost their ability to speak."

Now, be honest with me. How would you handle it if that's the way you spoke and you knew it, but there was absolutely nothing you could do about it?

I'll tell you how these two young guys handled it:

They laughed.

They laughed and laughed.

Nothing, in fact, could drive either one of them into wild fits of laughter more quickly than hearing the other's gibberish—which was identical, of course, to his own.

"You talk like you've got a f___ing mouthful of mashed potatoes [or rocks, or any number of crude or obscene objects]," one would say, and they would both rock back and forth so wildly in their laughter that one feared their wheelchairs might spill despite being locked into those special tracks built into the floor of the van.

Theirs was not high comedy.

"A regular Fibber McGee and Molly," my old Yankee grandma would have said.

Sometimes their word choices would disturb Father Jim or Gertrude (never, of course, the red-haired, foul-mouthed Gina).

The sound of their laughter was harsh and disturbingly similar to that heard at the seal pond of your local zoo, and to the sounds coming from the room of Eddie, the Fireman Who Barks Like a Dog.

Eddie, incidentally, had begun to quiet down at about this point and so he was invited, along with Trevor Howard, Tom Cruise, and me, to go sailing.

At about eleven o'clock one morning we were each handed a bag lunch from the kitchen, then loaded onto the invalid coach and whisked away to the docks on Long Island Sound. I was held fast by two burly male helpers who guided my legs, one at a time, then my torso, into the boat. Trevor and Tom were in considerably worse condition than I, and so their entire chairs, themselves included, had to be loaded onto the boat by means of a winch. The chairs were hoisted high above by chains, then swung around and gently lowered by the volunteer sailors who, judging from their expertise, might have been longshoremen. The chairs were lowered slowly, slowly; then Tom and Trevor were slipped out of their chairs completely and into some safety seats.

As the boat glided slowly out of the little harbor, we all used mental imaging techniques to picture our unhappy, anxiety-ridden selves being left behind on the dock as our newly released inner selves, our real and untroubled selves, slid slowly and gamely through the lightly lapping waves on the peaceful sound.

Eddie the Fireman remained on his very best behavior under the circumstances. The others, including Charlie, had opted not to come.

The deliberately uneventful trip gave us a gift of serenity, and we all expressed deep gratitude to the volunteer sailors who'd donated their time and expert sailing talents to help a bunch of bunion-heads. Their generous gift made me think of lessons I learned in Sunday school:

- *Feed the starving.*
- *Give alms to the poor.*
- *Visit the sick.*
- *Clothe the naked.*
- *Bury the dead.*

To which I added:

- *Take the ailing sailing.*

Not hysterically funny, right? But my young friends Tom and Trevor certainly thought so. They laughed hysterically, rocking the boat precipitously in their frankly hideous enthusiasm.

"What a great audience," I remember thinking. "Uncle Miltie would love these guys."

Most satisfying is that their laughter, at all times, was aimed completely at themselves.

Even today, when it is tempting to feel depressed or sorry for myself I think instead of these two young men. Will either of them become well enough to attract the opposite sex, as I have? To have a career, as I did? To marry, father a family, and lead a rich, full life, as I did? These questions always work when I am feeling low, because then I think of that funny, happy, uncomplaining team of Tom Cruise and Trevor Howard, and it becomes impossible not to realize how lucky I truly, truly am.

* * *

The notion of escape now seems absurd. Yet it is easy to recall the many disjointed, illogical feelings I had during the murky twilight that enveloped me and my fellow campers that summer. This is illustrated in a journal entry made as summer grew high and unrest grew deep.

> *June 5, 1992.* God, this place can get on your nerves. No one except Georgette will ever give me a push, and the only place she'll take me is to therapies. The rest of the time I'm on my own. The theory is that while the reality may be painful, none of us knows if we will ever be without a wheelchair. Therefore, we have to learn how to get around. Every person on the staff has some excuse for not being able to push you to the dayroom, say, or the telephones. It's always:
>
> "Sorry, my hands are full."

"Sorry, I'm rushing to conference."

"Sorry, I'm being paged."

"Hold that elevator!"

And always, always, you're left in someone's dust, pushing your chair by the wheel rim with your one good hand, using your one good foot for speed and doing your level best to avoid crashing into Gina, who so often stands in the middle of the hall with one foot nailed to the floor, rocking back and forth in a circle, cursing everything and everybody as she dances her Hemorrhagic Hop. And if it's not a direct head-on with Gina you're avoiding, it's another potential traffic disaster with Eddie, the Fireman Who Barks Like a Dog.

Just found out something really terrible about Eddie: Seems ol' Ed, rescuer of helpless dowagers and little girls with Cabbage Patch Kids, was no hero at all. No, sir. The reason he fell down that air shaft, if Gertrude is to be believed, is that he was trying to carry some stolen merchandise across to a hiding place where it could be stored for pickup after the fire.

Oh, man.

Do I ever want to go home.

There's no telling how true that story is about Eddie. I never quite believed it, but it had a strong negative effect on me and on all those who were struggling for something positive to hold on to.

One encouraging new friendship that bloomed suddenly at this time, however, was with Jack, the social therapist. Jack was a friendly, secure-seeming, all-around good guy whose job was to help us reenter the normal course of human interaction instead of turning into nonreactive, terminally depressed TV junkies.

He is the kind of guy my dad would say is "a prince of a man" or "a real Johnny-at-the-pump."

Jack, apart from gladly giving the old wheelchair a push at any time, was always great for a suggestion on how to spend an evening.

A hot little Pokeno game with a group of bloodthirsty octogenarians, say. Or a one-on-one trip to the shopping mall, frozen yogurt included. Or a "Night at the Races," which involved us tossing dice and Jack moving large plywood "horses" the given number of spaces on the gym floor as everyone was supposed to yell and cheer.

Then we would all have a nice piece of cake and go to bed exhausted.

Party, party, party.

* * *

One morning, while waiting for Mary Michael and my parents at the elevator (it really *was* a Friday), Charlie the Baker rolled up with the breathless announcement:

"They've got straitjackets!"

"What?"

"You heard me, Phil! Just saw two of 'em!"

Charlie, who had either forgotten my name or never knew it, did not call me Phil all the time. Sometimes it was Paul. Or Bill. Or Jerry. Never, never, it seemed, did he come upon Peter, even by accident.

"One of the straitjackets is for me, I know it! And I'll just bet the other's got your name on it, Bob!"

"Think of it, Charlie," I said, "they've got to keep straitjackets on hand in case somebody gets really wild or violent. Like that fireman, maybe, or who the hell knows?"

"Yeah, well, you just better listen to me and do what I tell you, or you'll be doing life in this joint without parole! Is this how you want to spend the rest of your life?"

Swimming? I thought. *Eating great food? Exercising every day in a fully equipped gym? Sailing on Long Island Sound? A living hell!*

At that moment Father Jim rolled by, mumbling in great annoyance over the menu choices he had just submitted for the next day.

"E-Z Whip! Can you imagine that? If it were just regular *Easy* I might have had some, but who in the heck can eat something spelled *E-Z?* Not this old marine, I'll tell you."

On and on Father Jim went about the ills of our society, so many of which (according to his theories) stem from "society's willful pandering to the least-educated, the laziest, and the lowest."

"How can our society ever succeed when it is by nature so permissive that it is downright sloppy? How long can we go on permitting even the august CNN to continue reporting things like 'The media *was* there' instead of 'The media *were* there'? Does Ted Turner have any standards at all? Does anyone? Everywhere you look, people are being downright loose about double negatives, shamelessly splitting infinitives and dangling their participles without a care! Now, I believe in a free society, but really, this is too much!"

I could hardly believe what was happening. I had come down to wait for my family's arrival and was dealing instead with a former baker who was now a convicted felon planning his escape from the stir, and with a singing Protestant minister who, although suddenly and disarmingly crooning a loud, deeply melancholic verse of "That Old Gang of Mine," seemed actually on the verge of advocating the violent overthrow of our government on the grounds of bad grammar!

Yet throughout those early summer months, throughout the singing bouts and grammatical correction bouts and the complaining bouts from Willie the Whiner and the schoolboy behavior of Ernie and the animal noises from Ed and the mothering from Gert and the near-hysterical worry about the rape of my wife and daughter and the bizarre, haunting memories of some other world I'd seen, something barely perceptible was happening:

I was getting better.

Not that one could notice. I still had plenty of weakness and a tendency to crash into anyone in the vicinity when I "walked," my mental state was definitely still fogged in, and I still couldn't whistle. But slowly, gingerly, the road toward walking had begun without the need of those ramps and guide rails (which Willie the Whiner assured me, at any rate, were about to collapse because they were "shoddy merchandise").

On one memorable day, Judy and Susan, acting as props on either side, began walking me back and forth, with further help from a four-legged cane. Occasionally Judy, then Susan, then both, would pull back to see what I could manage. I was weak and wobbly as a newborn colt, but hey!

I could do it!

There would be life, after all, without that damned chair!

Much as I wanted that accursed chair, symbol of all that was not right, to evaporate, I was still forced to use it for transportation. Once at a destination, I could sometimes get out of it. In the shower, for example, I could now get up to soap down and rinse while grabbing onto the safety bars with my good hand. But then it was back to the chair, where my derriere would remain super-glued until the next destination. I still could not walk on my own.

"Just do it!" I can recall saying in one of a series of lectures to my legs. "You've done it before, you can do it again, so none of this nonsense. Just do it!" The legs also drew inspiration, I felt, from my frequent renditions of such ditties as "Walk on By," "Walkin' in the Rain," and a 1960s golden oldie called "Walk

Like a Man." I even got a little sappy with Rodgers and Hammerstein's "You'll Never Walk Alone."

I was behaving like a latter-day Father Jim but, hey, it was worth a shot.

The early summer of 1992 was bleak and black in the Northeast, and mornings were rarely filled with their usual bright summer light. On one such morning, passing a nurses' aide named Julia on the way back to my room from the shower, I grumbled a good morning, followed by a typically brilliant bon mot:

"Another Blue Monday, hey, Julia?"

Reaching the entry to my room, I heard Julia's sweet, high-pitched voice calling back.

"Peter," she called, and I turned my wheelchair to face her. "It's Friday."

Friday! Hot damn! The one day I forgot to think it was Friday, it actually was Friday. Was I getting better? Or falling deeper into the category of the mentally ill? But who wanted to analyze? It was Friday, after all, and that meant Mary Michael! My family! Hot dog!

My new friend, Jack, the social therapist, happened by in time to give me a push to the outdoor cloistered area where some patients were permitted to wait for the arrival of family. Sitting there, craning to spot the arrival of Dad's new van (he had bought it with his unspectacular retirement income so that he would be able to take me places with my wheelchair), I found that my mind again began to wander.

The mental wandering took the form of another imaginary walk with Dad and Spike. This was particularly pleasant, because in this fantasy, the damned wheelchair was no longer needed. Mary Michael was with us too, and so she and I ran alone to the top of a hill just past a wooded glen. Spike ran, jumped, and snapped playfully at my cuffs, forcing me down. As I grabbed Mary Michael for balance, my weight forced her down on top of me. We held each other tightly and kissed as, together, we rolled into some hidden spot, our sense of romance as enkindled as if we were in some perfume commercial with Mary in a floppy hat with long, flowing ribbons and I holding a gift of flowers, running after her in slo-mo.

Cornball, yes, and this was clearly a legacy of the old soap opera days. But this bright, sunny pink reverie was my first romantic notion in more than three months of yellow-gray slur, and, while medication interfered with the thoughts ever becoming downright sexual, it was great to feel alive, even in my imagination.

Dad whistled in the distance for Spike as, in real time, I tried my own special "Spike" whistle. Lips pulled back, tongue interjecting just so, I took a deep breath and blew, casting off a fine mist along with a huge Bronx cheer. Nothing even close to a whistle. I tried again. No good. The left side of my mouth, while no longer spewing quite so many food items at mealtime, would be useless in calling my bright little dog.

In my reverie again, Dad was now calling *me* back to continue the imaginary walk with him and Spike around Gaylord's estatelike grounds.

As we walked, he talked of a woman who had repeatedly and, it seemed, deliberately, cut him off on the drive up.

"I tell you, Pete," he was saying, exactly as he'd said so often, "there ain't no such thing no more as 'courtesy of the road.' You remember when I was teachin' you to drive, people would wait for you, give you a chance to maneuver, even wave you on when you needed a little break? Today it's 'Me first and screw you.' You know who I blame? The politicians! It's everything for the rich. More, more, more! While us poor slobs on the bottom keep waiting for a little something to, what do they call it?"

"Trickle down, Dad."

"Yeah, that's it. 'Trickle down.' Imagine the nerve! It's like we have to say, 'Please give us the crumbs from your table.' Nobody likes that! Imagine these guys tellin' the poor working stiff he's got to be happy with somebody else's leftovers? And you wonder why everybody's crazy today? Why they got no values? Why nobody's got God no more? It's not because you can't say a prayer in your school. It's because of them bums in Washington who only think, 'Gimme, gimme, gimme'! I say throw 'em the hell out and let 'em learn how to work for a living!"

There was no arguing with that, even in fantasy. At that point Mary Michael reentered my little dream. She threw me a ball and I tossed it back with my left arm, which in reality was still as stiff as, well, a stiff's. At one point the imaginary ball bounced under the real bench near my wheelchair. Absentmindedly, I reached behind the bench for it in real time, and . . . and . . .

A Chunky candy bar! Half-eaten, covered with ants, the chocolate turned white and chalky as it crumbled in my hand, and the ants crawled up my right arm while I was unable to wipe them off with my left. One of Ernie's secret caches!

I am not a man who cries. But suddenly, an overwhelming swell of emotion erupted from somewhere in my chest. Tears began to dribble and I, Peter Swet, became wracked in sobs.

Was it the insects? Don't be silly.

Was it the little daydream in which I'd indulged? Yes, partially, but it was also the loosening of emotional control that can happen with brain-injured patients, and it was happening with me.

It wasn't the ants that were troubling. It was the fact that I could not remove them without help. And the corny little dream about Mary Michael certainly set up an emotional edge. I wanted her, wanted everything about her. And I ached to be with my fine young son and my beautiful young daughter. Floating atop this mental chaos at all times was one unconquerable and relentless thought:

Oh, God, I want to go home.

Such was my mental state one evening when I was approached by Charlie. He had been scheduled to join me and a group of other madcap fun lovers in an evening of unparalleled frolic down in the cafeteria. On this night, as on several others, a fairly effective bit of magic would be pulled off. The staid old characterless cafeteria, your basic green-and-gray issue, was being converted via flowers, candles, and atmospheric decorations into an evocation of a restaurant as seen on "the outside." It was here we were all invited to take our evening meal.

Charlie, however, had one of those "I have a secret plan" looks some of us had noticed on his face just prior to many previous evenings when we'd heard an alarm bell and then someone's wheelchair whizzing down the hall, followed by the thundering footfall of staff racing by and yelling, "Charlie! Charlie, stop! Charlie!"

"We have to talk," Charlie said, urging me with a crook of the head toward a small private balcony where, at that moment, the early summer sun was setting and the dampness was rising, covering the hushed, lovely evening in a dim twilight.

Whippoorwills whipped.

Crickets cricked.

Cicadas chicked.

From a distant hall, Father Jim could be heard:

"When whippoorwills call,
And evening is nigh,"

he crooned, concluding with a thickly nasal theatrical flourish:

"I hurry to Moy Ba-loo Heavonnn."

The door to the special "restaurant" in the cafeteria could be heard closing behind his wheelchair as he continued.

"They'll miss us," I said.

"We'll join them before they know we're here," Charlie continued with a hushed, childlike enthusiasm. "Do you know what the Indians used to call this place?"

"What?"

"The Valley of the Snow Leopard."

"Valley of the . . ."

"Ever seen a snow leopard?"

"Once, in the Bronx Zoo. I think. Ever been to the Bronx Zoo, Charlie?"

"Oh, no. No changing subjects. The snow leopard is one of the most stunningly beautiful beasts in all creation. Snow white. Blindingly white. Except, of course, for spots. And you know where they used to live?"

"You're, uhm, going to say here, aren't you?"

"Bingo!"

"But—"

"I know. I know it sounds weird, but I've given it lots of thought. You're familiar with continental drift, of course," Charlie said.

"Sure, that's how kangaroos, koalas, and so many marsupials wound up in Australia but nowhere else."

"Well, that's exactly what happened here. See, Africa was once part of North America. Just look at a globe, you'll see how it fits in. But when the continents drifted, one group from one species—the snow leopard—got stranded right here in what is present-day Connecticut. Most people don't know that, Dave, just me. And now, you.

"Take a good look out there. Tell me what you see. Tell me if you hear anything."

I listened, straining, wanting very much to be part of Charlie's sacred moment. That fine mist had snuggled even deeper into the sloping landscape, and with it came a slight chill.

"Sorry, Charlie. All I hear is that big air conditioner down by the gym."

"Don't worry. The snow leopard will call. The timing has to be perfect."

I listened again, straining every cell in my auditory canals. All was silent. But then, suddenly, through a not-so-distant window, I did hear something:

"Abba-dabba-dabba-dabba-dabba-dabba-dab,
Said the monkey to the chimp.

Abba-dabba-dabba-dabba-dabba-dabba-dab,
Said the chimp-y to the monk.

All day long they would jabber away,
All day long they were happy and gay.
Singin'
And swingin'
In their monk-ey tonk-ey way . . ."

"I hear something," I told Charlie.

"Father Jim," he answered with a grunt. "He can't come. He sings too much. But you can come, Albert," he said, "just as soon as you hear the call."

"How will I know what it is?" I asked.

"You'll know," he said simply.

"What happens when it comes?"

"You answer," Charlie said, as if talking to a very small child or an idiot. "You follow." He looked out over the deepening shadows where nothing could be heard now except for some crickets. He continued.

"Answering the call of the snow leopard leads to health, it leads to happiness, and you know what else?"

"What?"

"It leads to freedom! Look again, Joel! Look out there! Look!"

I again looked off the balcony and into that lovely valley, which now, even with darkness enclosing, seemed perfectly verdant because of Charlie's enthusiasm, his description, his sense of hope and belief. Like me, Charlie wanted to get out of here. Unlike me, he thought escape was our best bet.

Let me attempt an explanation of my own mental state, if not Charlie's, at this time:

Lacking any full memory of what brought me here, and feeling fuzzy at all times because of the haze brought on by my blood pressure medication, I found it damned hard to crack a good, honest thought of my own.

I had become "institutionalized"; that is to say, I had completely bought the program of being in an institution and, like someone who'd been brainwashed by the enemy, there was little to be done about it. If someone said "sit there and wait," I would sit there and wait, and it wouldn't occur to me not to. Along with that massive loss of brain cells a few months before went a sense of self, and it was up to Gaylord to help locate that along with teaching me to walk, touch, think, and feel.

What Jack, the social therapist, did almost every day was to involve us in situations that would give us a sense of choice, feelings of like and dislike, and the permission to just be our old selves. So if I didn't want to run off to "A Night at the Races" with my new buddies, that was okay with Jack. Respecting our decisions showed us that we were capable of individual preferences and choices, and that one day we might be whole again.

Somewhere along the line, however, Charlie had veered rather widely from the program. Tonight he was hatching his escape and wanted me to be part of it. Would I? I summoned my deepest sense of machismo, drawing upon some rock-solid wellspring of decisiveness and certitude to deliver my boldly heroic decision:

"I . . . don't . . . know," I said.

"Just think, Ben," he continued, arguing, "all you have to do is answer, and you enter a world like, who's that painter?"

"Rousseau," I said.

"Yeah, and you know what kind of world that is, don't you? It's a world where you're surrounded by peace and beauty. A world where no one harms anyone, so there's never anything like a head injury. It's a beautiful world, a gorgeous world. What you can do is, you'll work with me right here in my mom and pop's bakery, and you'll live here too. Come on, now, what do you say? Will you go with me, Saul? Will you?"

I could feel my nostrils flaring as, heaving my chest to its fullest, I glared at him manfully in the eye and issued a decision that, once rendered, I knew would remain forever implacable.

"We'll see," I said.

7

The Room of Special Purpose

1992 was an Olympics summer with reminders of that everywhere, and it sometimes seemed that the achievements of we detainees, no matter how insignificant to others, were as worthwhile as any of the bronze, silver, or gold that Barcelona had to offer.

My first medal, a bronze, was conferred one morning when I wheeled back to my room in search of the Memory Book, which, of course, had again been forgotten.

Whizzing down past the nurses' station and past the dayroom, I made a hard left down the hallway past the rooms with their large, block-lettered signs that had read:

Ernies Room

and:

Eddies Room

but that had been hand-changed by Father Jim to:

Ernie's Room

and:

Eddie's Room

from which emanated sounds like those in the film version of *Jurassic Park,* leaving me to wonder if Eddie the Fireman was now working in Dolby.

Finally, I came to the room with the sign reading

Peter's Room

Here, however, the hallway was blocked by a large four-poster bed enclosed in a corded mesh screen of ersatz chicken wire—my cage! It was being removed!

Unbeknownst to me, some message had passed somewhere that with my late-night behavior evidently improving, the cage was no longer necessary. I peered inside the room. Sure enough, the cage had been replaced by a standard, motorized hospital bed.

Trumpets blared. The white flag bearing the Olympic rings and colors unfurled. I meekly bowed my head and right there in the Gaylord hallway accepted my bronze, knowing that a gold, to be accomplished upon being rid of my wheelchair, could not be far off.

From that point on, leg exercises were accomplished with new vigor and resolve. I took extra time on the motorized bikes; when no one was looking, I would sometimes let go of the safety grip while using the treadmill.

I even broke into solo versions of "If You Knew Susie" while performing extra sets of the "windshield wiper."

Despite no change in forecast for that drippy, dreary June, plans were announced for Gaylord's annual Robert W. Barrett Outdoor Sports Clinic. At the time of the announcement, Ernie,

Father Jim, and I were finishing our daily physical therapy along with Willie the Whiner and Our Boy Hadjo, both of whom had now joined the routine. I was glad to see Hadjo, who'd apparently been under some separate program since his arrival. He had graduated from his wheelchair but still seemed deeply attached to that T-shirt bearing the map of Cambodia. His head was still the same size as the map, of course, and Willie the Whiner was still, well, Willie the Whiner.

We'd finished our individual stretchings and calisthenic drills and were now on the indoor basketball court, with Ernie tossing in *swoosh* after *swoosh.* Such moments never failed to leave me with a sinking feeling of both loss and inadequacy. I had never been a sport; never a person who knew how to take the ball and run with it. Still, it is something I had always wanted: Would I now, even at age forty-nine, finally allow that moment to come?

Sure, I told myself. *What the hell? Your balance and timing are off, stamina's shot, judgment's iffy, but so is everyone else's. This is your chance!*

Here was something I had not experienced since the age of four, when I'd failed miserably: a level playing field! Yes, I would join this sports clinic and, for once in my life, be like the other guys. My attitude was childish, I knew even then, but sometimes, well, a guy's just got to do what he's got to do.

The clinic organizers (Jack, our social therapist, and Rudy, our sailing skipper) showed up to make the announcement. Susan, our assistant physical therapist, handed out schedules.

Ernie looked at his copy with annoyance bordering on rage.

"No basketball? What are you guys trying to do to us?" he demanded. "You lock us in this place with someone watching over us day and night! You have my wife take away my *Penthouse* magazines (you think I don't know about that)? You yell bloody murder about a few lousy pizza slices under the bed. You won't let us wager a lousy buck at these so-called Nights at the Races."

"Don't forget the turkey gravy," Willie the Whiner interjected. "It wasn't just cold last week, it was lumpy! And that meat loaf!"

Ignoring Willie's whines, Ernie continued in a fury that could be sated only when it was agreed that basketball would be added to the schedule despite the fact that this was a summer clinic and basketball is an indoor winter sport. I looked up to notice Judy, our chief physical therapist, whisper to Hadjo, who nodded and pushed his wheelchair to follow her into the mysterious little room just off the gym.

Ernie, meanwhile, punctuated his victory over the authorities by flawlessly hitting hoop after hoop from his wheelchair and was quickly lusted after by the same group he'd just won over in his bid to add wheelchair basketball to the list of sports in the clinic. Ernie was, in fact, hounded and slathered over in much the same way high school hoop stars are hounded and slathered over by scouts from big-time basketball colleges. Nobody seemed to care about the malted balls or gummy bears in his pockets. And it made no difference when he started shouting, "Gimme an E, gimme an R . . ." senselessly spelling out the old cheer for Erasmus Hall, his high school alma mater in Flatbush, Brooklyn.

Suddenly, a bloodcurdling shriek drifted over the gym floor. It was the sound of horror mixed with fathomless pain and terror, the likes of which might have been heard in London's West End during Jack the Ripper's heyday.

The whacking sound of the ball Ernie had been dribbling stopped.

The whir of exercycles and walking machines and every other exercise machine stopped.

The buzz of conversation stopped.

Every noise in the gym stopped.

Another shriek drifted overhead.

"Hadjo!" someone said, and we all shot glances toward the little room. Sure enough, another scream. Sure enough, it came from that room. We all knew it was Hadjo.

Judy, nonplussed and obviously covering, told us it was now time for most of us to go to our next therapy and so, obedient little institutionalized brainwashees that we were, we quietly prepared to leave.

My next therapy was activities of daily living on Easy Street. It was also Willie's.

"I really like Easy Street," he said, as we transferred from wheelchairs to the waiting benches. "Maybe it has something to do with the name."

Aha! He recognizes his love of anything containing the word easy. *A rare moment of candor from Willie the Whiner*? I thought to myself.

"There's just one problem," he said.

Okay, here it comes.

"When you order things at the so-called lunch counter, they should give you real lunch instead of so-called lunch."

"But you go to real lunch right afterward," I said.

"You call that lunch?" he continued.

Dope! I thought, *Dummy! You handed him an opening as wide as Berle would give Jessel. And naturally he's driving right through it!*

"First of all, you can't even get a hotdog."

You deserve this. You brought it on yourself.

"You really want that?" I asked out loud. "Ground up chicken beaks and bull foreskins?"

"You go kosher, you do better. I'm gonna tell them I'm Jewish."

"The first person who ever changed religions over a hotdog," I cracked.

"It's worth it," Willie shot back, and I knew he believed that, so I kept my mouth shut.

Within a few moments we were inside the small therapy room on Easy Street, where I asked Carolyn, our occupational therapist, what happened to Gertrude, Mother of All Mothers, who had once so happily sat at the head of the table.

"Gone home," Carolyn said. "Isn't that nice?"

We all agreed that was nice.

"Probably got salmonella from the chicken gravy," Willie said, while in my own thoughts I sought a corollary between a patient's disappearance and the bloodcurdling shrieks heard from that little room off the gym. Were people tortured there? Did Gertrude really go home? Or was she taken to that mysterious little chamber, after which she simply disappeared?

* * *

Another word about brain damage:

One of the brain's basic jobs is to make sense of the world. Even when the brain is damaged, it needs to try to make sense of how the world functions, even if its conclusions are erroneous. Early on, for example, my brain perceived that I was in a hospital, that I was strapped into a bed, and that someone screamed the whole night long. The "sense" it made of this was that the screaming came from someone whose internal organs were being ripped out to be sold on the black market and that, logically, my turn would come. This sounds like delirium, but it isn't.

It's called confabulation.

Charlie confabulated, as you'll recall, that we all lived in a large commercial bakery where the women baked and the men drove delivery trucks. Gertrude confabulated an organized, sane world where mother calmly presided (until, that is, her safety seemed compromised by an intruder to her inner sanctum). Ernie, whose confabulations were actually less intense than most others, had contrived a harmless world of high school sports, childish pranks, hidden treats, and girls.

Sometimes a patient's confabulations were so intense that they would continue despite plain evidence to the contrary. I knew on one basic level, for example, that Gaylord was a fine hospital and that we were all quite safe and that my condition was slowly improving. I also knew that, like Gertrude, you eventually went home. On another level, however, there was still immense confusion: Was this, perhaps, a prison? Had I committed some serious crime? Worst of all was the gnawing fear that persisted, even in serene moments, that my family had placed me into an insane asylum and that the moment would come when I, too, would finally recognize a basic fact: that I was truly, incontrovertibly, and hopelessly insane. These contrary perceptions of reality often existed at the very same time and often seemed to do battle with each other for the truth. In this, I was no different from anyone else.

We were, all of us, strangers in a strange land trying our best to understand and survive.

Inside that little therapy room on Easy Street, a woman we had never seen before joined our group. Quite elderly, she suffered from an advanced case of arthritis. (I would learn later that in addition to specialization in brain damage and one or two other select areas, Gaylord treats those suffering the crippling effects of arthritis.) June Ann was one of those sufferers.

A curious thing about June Ann was that she seemed so worried about her hat. For example, when she found something to be very funny and began to laugh, she would sometimes gasp, "Oh! My hat!" Or she might say about our handsome young

Tom Cruise, "That boy looks like a real hat-breaker." Sometimes she talked about having had a hat attack. Or she might describe a meal as having been terribly "hatty."

Then one day she told us of having been an actress as a girl and having played the pat of Desdemona.

The pat of Desdemona, I wondered, *is that anything like the Thane of Cawdor? The Strait of Hormuz? The thief of Baghdad?* But I finally put it together. June Ann was what my old Yankee grandma would have called a "true Yank," hailing from northern Massachusetts. But poor June Ann. Her arms, wrists, and fingers were all twisted and bent, far worse than my own bundle of twigs. Her arthritis, it seemed, was systemic.

Willie chose this particular session to complain, once again, about the lack of facilities for such activities as woodburning. Macramé. Watercolors. Finger painting.

"Now that's what you call real therapy," he said again and again. "Not running around some gym like a bunch of idiot kids."

It had been explained several times to Willie that we were all receiving the therapies that best addressed our individual "deficits," but this didn't stop him.

"Look! You see this?" he said in a tone of petulance that by now was familiar to everyone. "This is what you call real therapy!" He was referring to a small, pretty, and surprisingly intricate stained-glass swan that was perfect for hanging in a window.

"Of course, I could never make something like this," he said in a familiar retreat to his whiny self. "Not with, you know, the pain."

We all knew this was nonsense. Except for June Ann, we all shared the same deficits, and, while we each lacked motion in at least one of our hands, we experienced no pain, either.

"That swan is beautiful," he said, momentarily feeling generous enough to issue a rare compliment. "Who made it?"

June Ann forced her gnarled, broken hands across the table. Slowly, achingly, she located the thin string and pulled the swan aloft, allowing it to slowly twist, its colors sparkling and twinkling as it caught light. She smiled beautifully, then with great pride and not a hint of malice turned to face Willie.

"I did," she said quietly.

Zing! Got him! I said to myself. *Atta girl, June Ann!*

June Ann may have been old and feeble and bent. She may have had gnarly, twisted hands. And it may have taken her time to catch on to things, like the rest of us. But unlike the rest of us, she never seemed to get angry or disgusted with Willie, no matter how he whined. Yep. There's one thing you could say about June Ann, all right:

June Ann had hat.

On one of the rare mornings that the sun actually shone that summer, I climbed out of my new regulation-issue hospital bed in which I had just slept without incident and looked out the window to see a whole raft of sports paraphernalia being assembled. A tennis net was strung across a parking lot and nets were being strung on the metal basketball hoops, with Ernie wheeling about, hiding treats, giving instructions, and generally getting in the way. A van had driven up and was now being conveniently placed for the disbursement of commemorative T-shirts as well as juices and soft drinks; a small tent containing tennis rackets, balls, and other sporting gear had been erected; and both Jack and Susie were laying chalk marks, writing on clipboards, and, in general, getting things ready.

Not too much earlier, such a scene would have filled me with dread, knowing that my sports inabilities would soon cause me to make a great fool of myself before peers. Now such things no longer mattered. Illuminated by this happy fact, my mind whizzed me back to the Ozone Park of my very early childhood and the event that caused such severe disdain for all sports.

The year was 1946 or 1947. Spike, of course, was far from being born, so it was just Dad and me. We were leaving the modest two-family working-class home with orange (yes, orange!) octagonal (yes, octagonal!) shingles where we lived on the second floor. Down the stairs we went, passing delicious smells of, let's see, what could Aunt Anna be cooking?

"Mmm, smells like lasagna," Dad said, and I knew we were all in for a treat that night.

"Well, if it ain't Pete and Re-Pete," Uncle Joe said as he left his downstairs flat and walked onto Atlantic Avenue behind us, closing (but in those days not locking) the front door.

"Where you boys goin' with your mitt and ball?" he said broadly, knowing that he was coaxing the obvious.

"I'm gonna play baseball, Uncle Joe!" I answered.

"You're learnin' from the best," he said. Dad was, unknown to his son at this early age, a star pitcher in the local softball league and a hero for miles around.

"Your father's gonna make you a star of the Brooklyn Dodgers!"

"Yankees, Joe. You know we like the Yankees," said Dad.

"We like the Yankees," I repeated.

"Okay, Yankees. You'll see, Peter. Some day that'll be *your* picture on Dixie cup lids, not Joe DiMaggio's. You know your ol' man's the best there is, don't you?"

"Yop," I said, using the Queens version of *yep*. "I know that, Uncle Joe."

We waved to Al and Adelaide, who were sweeping the sidewalk in front of the candy store across "the tracks" from Grandma's, then spotted Uncle Eddie and Uncle Danny, who, finished with their day's work of window washing, were headed for a couple of "brewskies" at the Woodhaven Lounge, our local "gin mill."

Uncle Eddie ran across the tracks toward us, carrying his

check for five dollars to Grandma Stine. In those days, five bucks was an ample contribution toward the care and feeding of one's mother (the monthly rent for the five-room flat where she raised nine children was, I recall, eleven dollars). Uncle Danny made the same contribution, and so did Uncle Freddie. Grandma was able to live comfortably.

On we walked past Old Man Dana's vegetable stand, where old man Dana could be seen tossing cups of cool water onto his sidewalk display of Italian plum tomatoes and parsley, peaches, lettuce, and bananas. He screwed his face, forcing his huge handlebar mustache into a twist as, up the street, a competitor's horse-driven cart clopped by, its driver shouting, "Ho! Bee-na-*no*! Ho! Bee-na-*no*," into the summer stillness, alerting any and all to the dangling "hands" of bananas, of which he hoped to rid himself by sunset.

This was still an era of neighborhood services, final vestiges of a style of life that had undoubtedly disappeared in other areas of the country by this time.

The umbrella man still plodded by regularly, ringing a bell and carrying a hand-driven machine that would repair any umbrella "good as new." The ice man still arrived by horse and cart to deliver huge blocks of ice to those who were not interested in, or could not afford, electric refrigerators. The knife man, pushing an odd device containing a specialized honing wheel, would pause periodically to sharpen anything whatsoever. The milkman was still a fixture in all neighborhoods; the ragpicker, in a horse cart fitted with a row of wildly jangling cowbells, would pay pennies or nickels by-the-pound for clothing of which you might wish to be divested. The Italian-ice man, seen only in summer, would turn the protective layer of burlap back from his huge block of ice and use a scoop-shaped ice shaver to dump the finely shaved ice into a paper cone, which he then coated with flavored syrup (this was the precursor to today's mechanized

Sno-Kone, which is not nearly as fine a product). In this memory, Dad had a cherry ice freshly shaved for me, then on we went past Otto & Tina's German deli, where Grandma would send me in later years to buy lunches of spiced ham, potato salad, and sweet gherkins, all for a total of twenty-five cents.

Continuing toward the park, Dad and I passed some local characters: Crazy Georgie, Charlie the Cripple, Fat Edie and her sister, Fat Anna (these, as noted, were pre-PC days). From Al Peretta's barbershop, strains of "Moonlight in Vermont" could be heard, followed by "Buttons and Bows," and then Al's very perky rendition of "How Much Is That Doggie in the Window?" during which he would actually make his violin bark.

Soon we arrived at the 88th Street Park, which is not a park as most people in America know parks. It is a square city block that had been leveled at some point, probably under the mayoralty of Fiorello La Guardia, "for the children of New York." The facility contained (and still contains, though the place is now shamefully run down) major attractions such as swings, monkey bars, a sand pit, seesaws, and more, all set under London planer trees surrounding a large kiddie pool. The pool had shower jets for cooling and splashing little neighborhood bodies that, in July, grew red as berries without any fear of cancer because the ozone layer—about which none of us had ever dreamed—was still intact. There was also a "park house" from which Sam the Parkie would sometimes emerge, red-faced and furious, demanding to know what "little devil" was so full of "monkeyshines" or "shenanigans" that he (never a she!) scribbled with crayon all over the Nok-Hockey set. We had a boys' room and a girls' room and a prominently placed flagpole around which we kids were expected to (and did!) gather each morning to solemnly salute our nation as its flag was raised. In the evening we would remain at stiff attention as the flag was lowered; then two of us would be chosen for the great honor of folding it in a precisely rehearsed triangulation manner and presenting it reverently back to Sam the Parkie for appropriate overnight storage.

At the far end, near the tracks, were eight handball courts. Between the playground and the courts were two small outdoor basketball courts and a large blacktop-covered area that was our goal and my destiny: the softball field!

Near some benches that rimmed the field, we met up with some of Dad's friends and fellow ballplayers, men with names like "Matches" and "Joey the Greek" and "Tommy the Polack" and "Kayo" and "Stosh" and "Toots." They all greeted Dad by the name "Satch," an honorific title bestowed because his style reminded them of the legendary pitcher Satchel Paige.

The image projected on my mind's movie screen shows me as a very little boy surrounded by friendly, hulking men with booming, merry voices. At the far end of this circle of shadows stands my dad, softball in hand. The ball is too large for my hands, so someone comes up with a small rubber "Spaw*deen*" (Queensish for *Spaulding*), which I am instructed to throw to Dad.

"No, no, no," he says. "That's not how you do it. Here. Here, watch me," he says, demonstrating in slo-mo the great style that had made him a local legend. I try, but cannot manage to throw the ball properly, and so we try again.

And again.

And again.

"Nah, nah, that's not the way, Peeda. Peeda, here! Here, watch! You're not watchin', Peeda. Look, Peeda, look!"

Dad, known almost as much for his patience as for his ferocious pitching ability, grows increasingly agitated and exasperated as his only son simply keeps failing and failing before all of his softball buddies.

"Nah, nah, you ain't doin' it right! Watch now, watch me!"

More tries. More failures.

"Nah, nah, Peeda, you can't do it! You ain't doin' it! *You're throwin' like a girl!*"

There it was. That single phrase, uttered in pure frustration in a single unthinking moment by this generous, forgiving, terrific man, would haunt his four-year-old son for decades.

I still recall the exact moment—the smells, the sounds, the feel of the breeze—when, bursting into furious tears, I took that Spaw*deen* and slammed it straight down onto the pavement, running away from the situation, and baseball, for the rest of my life.

For years afterward, I couldn't be induced to pick up a baseball, much less throw it to someone or catch it. And thus an otherwise typical, athletically built kid, son of a local sports hero, and perhaps highly talented himself (he would never know), turned forever from participation in and enjoyment of sports of any kind.

Until today.

Maybe the real reason I did not feel worried about the Robert W. Barrett Outdoor Sports Clinic was that having recently faced death and won, the possibility of losing face before a few fellow patients seemed pretty damned unimportant. Also, I had physical deficits, a perfect excuse.

Once more I noticed the buzz of sports activity in preparation below my hospital window. I sighed determinedly, preparing to take part in whatever would come my way. I was ready. "Gentlemen," I actually said aloud to myself in a non sequitur that somehow made sense, "start your engines!"

Nothing we did, as the day evolved, required much skill. The games were devised, remember, for paraplegics and quadriplegics. Technically and legally, of course, I was a paralytic. At an earlier point, Carolyn had tested sense perceptions by presenting my left arm and hand with various objects: a feather, a paper clip, something from the freezer, a slightly warmed cigarette lighter, and several other objects. Not only could I not name a single item; it was impossible to distinguish one from the other or to experience heat or cold or any sensation except, briefly, for some pressure she had applied from her own hand.

At the sports clinic I hit a few balls over the tennis net and then bagged a ball or two in the game Ernie had demanded be officially admitted to our little Olympics. Golf was not permitted for me and there was no chance of softball. Still, there came the moment when we were each presented with a T-shirt bearing the picture of a guy playing tennis from a wheelchair. Surrounding it was the logo "Advantage Wheelies." Bold letters on the back proclaimed, simply, "Robert W. Barrett Sports Clinic."

No medals had been won, but considering the little story you have just read, I did damn well, all right! I deserved to wear this bright yellow shirt telling the world that I, the kid who couldn't throw a ball straight, had now, finally, at age forty-nine, participated in a sports clinic and had earned the right to wear its T-shirt!

Not an Olympics moment, exactly. And no Olympic theme rang in my head as I pulled on that easily won shirt. What I did seem to hear, though, was the opening fanfare from *Also Sprach Zarathustra,* that hoary old war-torn piece brought to resurgent fame in *2001: A Space Odyssey* and used endlessly in television commercials ever since. The piece was intended by Strauss to underscore grand metaphysical change, an experience that in my case was damned well accurate. After forty-five years, here I was at last: Peter Swet Jr., sport! And with a T-shirt to prove it!

The next day we were back to our usual routine. As we went through our paces with Susan, Judy tapped me on the shoulder and pointed to that little room—the Room of Special Purpose.

It was my turn!

Outwardly, there was nothing sinister about the little room—just a room off the gym originally designed, perhaps, for rubdowns or as a potential private office or perhaps for private therapy.

Judy had helped "stretch" me before, a process that was painful in itself and that Carolyn preferred to avoid, and since Judy had no compunction about performing the necessary, I quite naturally referred to her as "Madame de Sade."

While serial casting had had some benign effect on this newel post that had been an arm, it was felt that Madame de Sade's brand of deep massage might provide further benefit.

She smiled a sweet, beautifully feminine smile as I climbed onto the cot and lay on my stomach as instructed. Soon her pummeling hands were at my left shoulder blade, where one or both of them soon began to dig. Deep. Then deeper. And deeper.

God knows what she was digging for, but she had lots of trouble finding it, and the deeper she went the more pain was involved.

By comparison with the gurgling, bloodcurdling shriek that blew out of my mouth, Hadjo had merely issued the occasional "ouch." Yes, it was pain. But I had felt something!

Judy knew that I jokingly called this place the "Room of Special Purpose," but not why. I explained that that was the name of the secret room that had been set aside by the Communist "Reds" circa 1918 for the bloody assassination of Czar Nicholas II and his wife, son, daughters, and servants. Willie the Whiner had caught on to this little joke and, apparently fearing some sort of staff conspiracy against patients, raced into the room, frightened and demanding to know what in hell this "special purpose" was.

"Relax," I said, "just deep massage. You may be next."

He insisted there was no way in hell he'd submit to "this bunch of kooks" and that if Judy so much as came near him, he'd call the authorities.

"Well, why the hell not?" I asked Judy.

I figured that a guy who'd change religions over a hotdog would have no compunctions about arresting a physical therapist over a Rolf job.

8

The Summer of the Crows

> *June 9, 1992.* Dreams grow crazier. Last night those knife-wielding potato-faced thugs dropped in again to threaten my wife and kids; then came all those haunting images about being in a place where internal organs were removed, without anesthesia, for sale on the black market; then a dream about George Bush winning the 1992 presidential race because so many people were grateful that he made it okay to hate broccoli. My most recently recurring dream involves, of all the world's population, reporter Christiane Amanpour.

The dream was troubling, but not because it was nightmarish—it wasn't. The very notion haunted me: Why Christiane Amanpour? Why my brain?

In the dream, I am in a curiously gelatinous terrain full of bending, twisting ridges and rises. It looks like one of those kiddie attractions you see at street fairs, a room with air-filled floors that appear to be made of a bicycle's inner tubes, and the fun is in attempting to walk or even stand on it. It is, of course, a mind's—*my* mind's—re-creation of a brain. *My* brain! I dreamed it, I now realize, because of the immense struggle with the very notion that I—*I*—had actually had brain surgery. My subconscious had reached for Christiane Amanpour because I had so respected her journalistic intrepidness during the Persian Gulf war, and I needed such a powerful image to absorb the reality of my own situation.

Now Christiane Amanpour was in my dreams, conducting a live broadcast from my living, throbbing brain and describing the above events on site and as they occurred to CNN Central's Bernard Shaw. The dream performed a great service, as many dreams do without our realizing it. In this case, Amanpour's explanations helped me visualize and accept that my brain had "exploded," as I invariably imaged it.

In the dream, Amanpour stood amid the rubble of dead and dying blood cells, dodging the blood clot just as neatly as she'd once dodged incoming Scud missiles. This made clear and immediate what had happened and how it was that I came to lose control over so much of my own body.

What it didn't make clear was why I, a forty-nine-year-old who'd lived at least half a life, remained alive and with some hope of a future while so many others, including a fourteen-year-old boy in our neighborhood who died from an aneurysm, a young person as full of life and promise as my own sweet Emily Kate, had been forced to call it quits.

"There's a greater power at work here," my dear old buddy Mike had said. I doubt this, since I don't believe in predestination now any more than I believed in God then. But sometimes you have to wonder.

And, speaking of my old buddy:

June 11, 1992. What's happening with Mike? I don't expect him to make the long trip up here, not with his wheezing and hacking and their accompanying terrors, but why doesn't he call? Why doesn't he sit down and write one of his funny letters?

I missed Mike tremendously. Dotson, too, of course, as well as all of my Westhampton writer friends. But Mike was special. Mike was a *mensch*—the affectionate Yiddish term for exceptionally good people. And my friendship was as important to him as was his to me, which is why his long silence was difficult to understand.

Mary Michael said he had taken my illness badly and had been very troubled by it, feeling that there was most definitely some higher purpose to this bizarre and inexplicable attack and that, furthermore, I had been spared for "a reason."

This notion was soon added to the many disjointed thoughts that continued racing and tumbling through an increasingly troubled brain.

June 12, 1992. Mike has died.

Mary Michael told me the last time she was here. He actually died shortly after I got sick but she, and perhaps the doctors, wanted me strong enough to accept the news and so she waited until I became insistent upon knowing why my old pal hadn't called or come to see me.

Mike had long been a victim of the emphysema that killed him. By the time he died, he was living in an airless vacuum, forced to strain for each gasp of air and, near the end, to travel about with an oxygen tank in the backseat of his Saab.

I first met Mike through a biweekly social gathering of

writers in Westhampton Beach, the same group through which I'd met wonderful friends like Dotson and Budd Schulberg and had had a brushing acquaintance with a number of America's greatest living writers as well as a host of unknowns like myself. Mike made an indelible impression at the first meeting by having four—four!—cigarettes going at the same time. I joked that this seemed like an old Sid Caesar routine, and Mike told me how he had been a writer-in-development at NBC during Caesar's day, working with people like Larry Gelbart, Norman Lear, and Mike's own boyhood pal Ed Simmons, a partner of Norman Lear's who had gone on to become the head writer and producer of *The Carol Burnett Show.*

Mike's addiction to cigarettes did not go gently into the night. He grunted. He groaned. He huffed and puffed and moaned a long, unspoken agony for one lousy drag, going on to use Nicorettes and patches and every nicotine-busting technique known to the human species, at the same time experiencing a lengthy, searing withdrawal that involved body aches, depression, dizziness, and irritability. With his yellow-stained fingertips, his sallow gray complexion, the stale odor that clung to his ash-flecked clothing, and the wheezing, hacking, phlegmy coughs that Ernie and his old Brooklyn high school buddies would have called "lung hockers," Mike had become an unwitting poster boy for the antismoking cause.

But he succeeded in quitting. It was his success, in fact, that inspired the end of my own lifelong addiction.

"If Mike can do it," I said to my wife, "anybody can."

And I did.

I loved Mike, and so not knowing of his death and being unable to attend (much less speak at) his memorial service cut me deeply. Dwelling on this disappointment some weeks later at Gaylord, I felt myself sliding into another depression. Joan,

Gaylord's resident psychiatrist, knew of my earlier full-blast bout with the illness, but did not know the details. Now she asked.

I told her that my one outstanding image was of crows. Big crows. Fat crows. Ugly crows. Crows all over the place, morning and night, making that god-awful caw-caw racket only crows can make. Because of the crows, it had been impossible to sleep in the impossibly hot afternoons of that impossible summer. The depression, at that point roaringly and searingly alive, though not yet identified, had made night sleep all but impossible.

I would begin an evening with a bit too much to drink. This is an ill-advised way (for me, for you, for anyone) to ease mental anguish, since alcohol is a depressant and in the end there is only one possible way to feel: worse. Then would come depression's attendant sleeplessness. I'd look at the clock and it would be, say, 2:00 A.M. Four or five hours would pass. I'd look again: 2:10!

With this drag of time came the pouring of night sweats onto swampy pillows; the endless, restless turning of the body; and the pretzel-knot twisting of sheets. My mind would rove again over worn-out, rutted terrain, pausing briefly at the face of each and every individual who had, whether by carelessness or design, caused actual or perceived harm. The continual panning of this mental camera would pause first at the face of the man who had taught me, a young and promising playwright, to make good money and support a family by writing soap operas, therefore quite innocently damning me to turn my back on the theatre I loved in favor of a world I came to despise. The mental camera would then move on to the faces of many other "soap types" who had learned to play the vicious corporate game of New York daytime TV so much better than I; on to the face of the new head writer on *Sesame Street*, a man whom I'd so resented that I performed poorly, spiting myself by losing the finest job (with the finest people) that a writer could wish for in New York television.

The camera panned to other writers I resented, some who were decent people just caught in the same soapy web but who handled it better than I; to New York theatre and TV agents whose friendship and support I had lost as if by personal design; to producers and other heads of soapdom, some of whom I have since learned to respect and admire as people who carved niches for themselves in the difficult and vicious world of daytime television; and even to those who, to their credit, made every effort to behave morally in an immoral universe.

We had moved, that summer of 1991, to a smaller, more modest house, which we rented for a relatively small sum, having been forced to rent out our own very pretty, very yuppie Westhampton home for the summer for income. The generated income, barely covering our home's monthly mortgage on top of rent for what was, in comparison, a dreary cottage, made the effort only marginally worthwhile.

The cottage, albeit with four bedrooms, was a cramped turn-of-the-century saltbox that had seemed altogether adequate upon signing the lease in spring, but in July and August, had proven inadequate, stuffy, cramped, and hot, hot, hot.

And every day, sometimes all day long, I heard crows. Crows at sunrise. Crows at noon. Fighting, yelling, insolent crows! Pecking, preening, squabbling crows! Crows on the front lawn, crows in back. Crows in the side yard. Crows, crows, crows!

Depression, for those who may not be aware, is one of the most misnamed maladies in medicine. We all feel "depressed" from time to time in the sense that it is human and natural to feel down because of a bad day at work, say, or to feel blue over some unfortunate love situation. True depression—clinical depression, once known as "melancholia"—is something more sinister, far deeper, and far, far more dangerous. It is a mental illness, sometimes terminal because it can seem that the only way to end your pain is to end your existence. It is caused by an imbalance of brain chemistry that is often triggered by a particularly searing event or series of events.

Writers, for reasons unknown, seem to suffer depression more than the general population. Art Buchwald is an example, along with the man whom I hold to be the finest living American writer, William Styron. Styron wrote an exceedingly valuable book on the subject, a book whose title alone clearly and immediately defines the illness of depression: *Darkness Visible.*

This certainly felt accurate in my case. I was, purely and simply, a wretch of a man who made life impossible for himself and exceedingly difficult for his loving, innocent family.

My behavior became odd and unreliable. Jokes and good-humored cracks no longer dotted my day. Paranoia reigned. And the cocktail time, with its promise of an hour's release, sometimes became a bit longer than it should have.

Depression is an excruciatingly ugly illness. Its trigger, in my case, was the Writers Guild of America television strike of 1988, which cut off my source of income for years, as it turned out, and which took effect on the very day we moved into our splendid new half-million-dollar home in the Hamptons. At the time, I was associate head writer of the daytime soap *Loving,* a job supposedly protected by union contract for at least another year. My contract, however, was dropped during the strike and the union simply failed to offer protection or intervention of any kind.

"It's a damned shame, Pete," one of the union's young attorneys actually said on one of the several occasions I called to complain of improper employer action, "but no matter how hard you try during these strikes, *some people just seem to fall between the cracks."*

There it was. The sentence that would haunt every waking moment for two years. Later, for the sake of my reemerging mental health and peace of soul, it became essential to find forgiveness for all who, intentionally or unintentionally, had created harm. This included that young Writers Guild attorney. He was, after all, simply a union employee whose ill-chosen, ill-timed, extraordinarily destructive remark was made in innocence and intended as a gesture of condolence.

That summer of 1991, peak time of a clinical depression that had been building since 1988, marked my second year as a contributor to *Parade*. The work with *Parade* proved to be personally crucial.

The Joan Rivers interview, during which I suspected my own depression, was quite successful, emboldening me to be relentlessly tenacious in convincing not-always-agreeable celebrities to agree to a personal profile. More important, that experience sent me to the library in search of a book that would help determine whether I, in fact, suffered from the depression that had killed Rivers's husband, Edgar. I drove to the library in nearby Hampton Bay for fear of alerting my own community to the possibility of my mental illness and thereby profoundly embarrassing my teenagers. There I located a text containing a self-administered test for depression. The results, scaring all hell out of me, sent me straight to a psychiatrist.

It is difficult for me to describe negatives, and most difficult to describe that most negative of human experiences, depression. However, I will try by asking you to spend a typical day of that period with me:

You awaken. Your eyes examine the ceiling as light streams in, and you are aware of pounding surf nearby. You hear that beautiful, full-throated mockingbird who sings every morning in counterpoint to the dull, pitiful sighing of the mourning doves.

"Not so bad today," you think, glancing out across a beautiful lawn that stretches to a croquet court being manicured for today's game on the estate beyond your hedge.

"Okay," you say, trying to convince yourself. "I can handle this."

You raise your head from the pillow, determining that today it's just not going to defeat you. You make it a rule: not today. You are happy to look for little successes the same way that an alcoholic does, one day at a time.

You place your feet on the floor. So far, so good. You're tired for lack of sleep, but hey, you'll nap later. Coffee's your first priority. On your way to the kitchen, you conduct a constant self-examination: Am I okay? Can I be productive, uphold the dad's end of a family contract by finding work, writing, bringing in that healthy income? Bringing in *any* income beyond the solid but highly irregular freelancing fees from *Parade*? "Sure," I lie to myself, "it's a new day. Sun's up, coffee's hot, so—*Excelsior!*"

Somewhere on the way to the kitchen, however, a dark gray curtain begins to descend.

"No!" you say, knowing that grayness will soon envelop and snuff the slender threads of yellow sun you'd so hoped might brighten your day, just this once.

"No! Not now! Not today! Let me be myself for one day, one stinking morning! Let me grab a toehold! Just once!"

But the familiar heavy curtain is already falling. It drops not so much in your line of vision as squarely on your shoulders. Slowly, slowly, and heavily, heavily.

You know immediately: Another day is shot. No resumes will be sent. No phone calls to the agent. No phone calls at all. Business is impossible. Life is impossible.

You can't face paying your bills, so they sit on your desk.

You can't face straightening out your insurance problems, so they sit there too. So does all that paperwork regarding foreign TV rights, royalties, and residuals; the pension, IRA plans, and mortgage papers. The future of your family is in miserable shape, but you are stymied and frozen, incapacitated by the unbearable darkness of being.

You can't ask for understanding, much less sympathy. How could anyone sympathize with a guy who's such a pathetic loser that he can't take care of his own wife and kids?

And you're stuck with yourself. Just you and these thoughts, roaring like an endless freight train through your brain.

The morning slips by filled with blackness.

And the sound of crows.

These fighting, nasty, brawling consumers of roadkill and carrion come to characterize all the empty, meaningless noise of your life. You cannot move in any direction. You gradually realize (and there is truth in this) that your wife, your kids, all your family and friends would be better off without you. At the same time, you suspect some failed genetic component has doomed you as a human being; it is this failed component that urges you toward the only solution guaranteeing that the mutation will no longer be passed on to future generations. It now presents the only option that makes sense:

Suicide.

While the Rivers interview made me realize the selfishness of suicide and its awful effects on one's kids, my blackest daydreams held such a grip that it seemed possible to find a way to kill myself, and therefore the pain, in a way that did not look like suicide. Driving to another town (this time Southampton), I bought the book *Final Exit,* hoping to find tips and techniques. Fortunately, the information it contained did not suit my needs.

More hot days. More sleepless nights. More blackness. More crows. The only true respite from all the heat, sleeplessness, and blackness of my own little *annus horibilis* proved to be an assignment from *Parade* for a personality profile on singer-composer Billy Joel, a celebrity whose presence I did not look forward to. Joel had been elusive and difficult to track down. This was the summer of his *Storm Front* album tour, which took him across the country and to many foreign locations, with stops in Seattle, Tacoma, and throughout the Northwest, an area of the country I'd never visited. I tried to set us up for Seattle. No go. Tacoma. No go. Portland. No go. It dawned on me that Joel lived in Easthampton, a short drive from my own home, but he claimed his family's personal life to be inviolable, so . . . no go.

We wound up in Cincinnati. Arriving there, I braced myself for handling an egocentric, domineering, Napoleon-complexed, all-too-typical rock-pop star and his entourage of bootlicking, cocaine-snorting, liquor-laden, furniture-breaking sycophants and toadies.

What I found instead was a hip, soft-spoken, kind, and generous man surrounded by a small, elite group of caring professionals whose job it was to put on the best damn show they could. Which is exactly what they did.

Over a late dinner after the show, Joel told me of another cross-country trip further back in time, a trip traveled alone and by bus. Down, out, and nearly ruined by promoters and quick-buck artists, he was returning to New York, the city he loved and the rest of the country loved to hate. It was the time of New York's near-default on bank notes and the Ford administration's refusal to guarantee those notes. It was the very day of the famous *New York Daily News* headline:

Ford to New York: Drop Dead

Traveling up Manhattan's West Side, Joel caught a glimpse of the Palisades on one side of the Hudson and, on his side, of the City's many elegant spires gleaming in the setting sun.

Instead of falling into the howling maw of depression over what had up to then been a tumultuous creative life, he whipped out his composition pad and in a single sitting wrote the wistful, jazzy "New York State of Mind."

* * *

I arrived back home in Westhampton to the same heat, the same unending blackness, and the same damned business with the crows, crows, crows. Yet I had learned something new. Joel, like Joan Rivers, had taken the worst that life had offered and turned it into something positive and shining. The lesson gnawed at me but, not yet realizing where an adulthood of godlessness had led me, I wasn't ready to adopt it.

I made yet another visit to an out-of-town library, this time to look through a *Physicians' Desk Reference* to locate an easily contracted illness that might prove fatal. When I handed the book back, the librarian said that I looked familiar. She recognized me as being from Westhampton Beach and then innocently asked my name. I dragged up an old pseudonym—Paul Samuels—used only once for a revolting made-for-TV movie I'd written for the Playboy channel.

That did it. The pure silliness of my intrigue caught up with me until finally, crossing the Hampton Bay library parking lot, I began to snicker. As I shook my head in amazement at myself and these desperate but silly straits, the snicker turned into a laugh. The laugh grew longer and louder. I was laughing foolishly, I knew, but still, *laughing!* And it was at myself!

What a fool, what a dope, what a boob for thinking I could kill myself without anyone knowing it was intentional. What a fool, what a dope, what a boob for thinking this was the best way of protecting my wife and kids. What a fool, what a dope, what a boob for wanting to stop living, no matter what the reason.

I, Peter Swet, resolved to recognize depression for the illness it is. And I would *do* something about it.

As I pulled into the driveway, the sound of crows was, as usual, everywhere. Two or three of them feasted on a dead possum as others fought to zoom in. The first step in my new mental stability crusade would be to get rid of this wretched crow situation, symbol of a life gone awry. I got on the phone with Bertel Bruun, who, in addition to being a distinguished neurologist, is an accomplished wildlife expert and co-author of *Birds of North America.* Surely Bertel would have some handy, ecology-wise tip for helping me achieve my goal. His joking response gave me another long laugh, my second in a single day:

"Got a gun?"

My next call was to Bertel's wife, Ruth, our psychiatrist-friend, who made room in her schedule to see me. After just a few sessions, it became clear that proper medication, as opposed to long, difficult (and terribly expensive) years of psychoanalysis would be the order of the day for my mental disorder. It was healing and very, very comforting to know that this terrible illness, destroyer of home life, family life, and all too often life, itself, is a quantifiable medical disorder. That means there is nothing wrong with the central "you," the inner "you." You are not a "bad" or "flawed" person composed of genetically inferior materials who therefore should best be destroyed. You are not doomed to never pick up and throw the ball of life. You are merely ill, damn it, in the same way that a person with a broken bone is ill. And what do you do when a bone is broken? Get it fixed!

There is no reason for anyone, ever, to remain in that deep pit of depression: Help is there for all. At that time it was in the form of the marvelous new drug known as Prozac; now newly spawned generations of medications represent even further advances. After several months and various alterations of dosage, my medication slowly, eventually began working. My many years of godlessness had culminated in these latter years of coldness, darkness, confusion, and loneliness. I didn't know it yet, of course, but soon I would be entering a very different world, one filled with warmth, light, and an all-pervasive love that will, I know, be with me through the rest of this life and then for eternity itself.

The first sign of normalcy was a return of sexual appetite. Then a cessation of suicidal thoughts, although "down" moods still prevailed.

Then, one spring day, while walking along the odd, right-angled curve in the front path of our old Westhampton house to which we now had happily returned, there came a "lifting," an almost miraculous raising of spirit to a level not known for perhaps two years.

Somehow in this one sweet, unforgettable moment it was simply, unmistakably over. The heavy gray curtain had risen to a sunny, leafy front lawn where huge pink buds were about to burst on the ornamental cherry trees, where the dogwoods had already begun opening their tiny crosses, and where the baby daffodils I'd planted for my beautiful daughter, Emily Kate, were in full, sweet, yellow bloom.

And what was this strange, undefinable sensation of the spirit? Could it be?

Yess! I was *me* again! Almost unidentifiable after that long, wearing journey, but alive. Upbeat. Feeling good. Back in our own home again. And without a crow in sight!

9

Night of the Living Dead

June 10, 1992, morning. I jogged!

That little entry may seem childish, but consider the joy and astonishment I felt when, wholly unable to stand or move my left leg or toes just three months earlier, I had been coaxed by the wizards of Gaylord into the miracle of standing; then of walking down a protected ramp; then of walking with a three-legged cane; then of walking unaided. Moments before writing "I jogged!" I had been taken to the gym's outer hallway and instructed to jog in place, which I did; then to jog a few feet, which I did; then to jog the full length of the hallway—about forty feet—which I did! *Yess!* The wheelchair would still have to be welded to my rear end for longer jaunts, but clearly, clearly, I was on my way! Truly my silver medal moment!

Yet all was not bliss. I still had plenty to worry about.

June 10, 1992, later. Now I know what Charlie was talking about the other day. I saw them—straitjackets!—in the chief of staff's office right across from the nurses' desk. Thank God they're letting me go home for Matt's graduation. Do I really have to come back here?

Strictly speaking, the items Charlie and I had seen were not straitjackets. They were another, less stringent form of restraint known as "posies," but a form of restraint they most certainly were, and, considering my feelings on the subject, I momentarily felt frozen in ice.

It didn't help that, slightly earlier, I had detected bizarre, stigmata-like scars on each foot. Had these quacks performed some strange, satanic ritual, perhaps when I was in that coma?

A 911 call to Mary Michael soon set things straight: During the initial reaction to brain injury, it seems, the brain orders various body parts to do things they are better off not doing. One confused order my brain gave my feet, for example, was to curl upward into a flexed position that would make later efforts to walk even more difficult. Therefore, my feet were placed in padded thongs with straps pulling downward and tied to the bed, thus preventing upward curl.

My built-in aversion to any form of restraint, however, had my feet pushing and rubbing constantly against the thongs, creating blisters that would heal, then form, then heal, and so on. Mary Michael's story made sense, all right, but so did my own theory involving black masses with key members of the staff in the basement at midnight.

The truth is that I was sick to death of all such thoughts, fears, and concerns. What I needed was simply to be home, to wake up with the smell of salt air and the sound of crashing waves, the feel of Mary Michael curling for warmth against my back and of Spike's cold wet nose nudging wakefulness by forcing my dangling hand into petting position.

Instead of the sleepy sweetnesses of home, what I had was a deranged version of "Five Foot Two."

and:

"What the f___ am I doin' here? Who do these mother-f____ers think they are, anyway?"

and:

"GrrROW, ROW ROW! Sss-SST!"

and:

"You call this oatmeal? For God's sake, I could do better with boiling water and a handful of sawdust!"

and:

"Moth-err! Moth-err!"

Note that by this time, although I had performed my own share of predawn yelling earlier, almost all of it actually did come from Charlie, whose recovery seemed terribly slow, mentally if not physically.

He had lost the use of an arm and a hand, as most of us had, but he no longer needed his wheelchair at all. This meant that a wholly new question based on Charlie's sudden freedom was now resounding through the dayroom, the hallways, the cafeteria, the gym, Easy Street, and just about every other place at Gaylord:

"Where's Charlie?"

* * *

Because most of its physical plant is built into a hillside, the layout of Gaylord Hospital is a ball of confusion for even the brain-healthy. The gym and cafeteria, for example, are both listed as being in the basement, but these facilities have windows opening onto patios and verandas, easily convincing one that one is on the first floor instead of in the basement.

This helps explain why I could never find Easy Street, why Ernie could never get to the outdoor basketball courts for his Bonamo's Turkish Taffee or his Tootsie Rolls, and why Father Jim could never find his Memory Book in the solarium. (It wasn't really the Memory Book that was lost—it was the solarium.)

One might, therefore, predict utter chaos when an emergency evacuation drill was ordered up.

Yet any weakness in such an exercise needed exposure and possible repair before it might actually become necessary, and so we received notice that a full-scale evacuation would occur on the following day at an unannounced time.

Charlie was ready for it.

He made several obscure remarks that afternoon about how we should "be ready," that "our time is coming," stuff like that.

I paid little heed. I was too busy rejoicing over my latest Olympic moment.

This moment occurred when, practicing with a cane now, I'd walked down to the dayroom for lunch. Going back to the room marked "Peter's Room," to look for my Memory Book, I found a new patient exiting my room, stealing a wheelchair. *My* wheelchair!

But wait. This was no new patient. It was a new orderly performing the task he'd been sent to do: retrieve the wheelchair from the room of a patient who no longer needed it. Me!

Fireworks! Marching bands! A little lighted box flashing "Applause!"

I strove for humility, however, as I lowered my head to accept my gold, the recorded version of "The Star-Spangled Banner" blaring in the background. There'd be no speeches or statements from yours truly, though. No waving to the folks back home. No peace signs, no power salutes, no secret winks to special someones. Just the eloquence of silence with a slight but unmistakable lowering of the eyelids in acknowledgment of humble but everlasting appreciation to a grateful nation.

Best of all, when I went home for my son's high school graduation, I could arrive there on my own two feet. *Yess!*

The day of the drill announcement dragged on endlessly. But the next day—the day of actual evacuation practice for several dozen patients with mush for brains like yours truly—flew speedily.

Breakfast occurred without incident except for Gina breaking her long refusal to talk to me. Overhearing me mention to another patient that my wife is Italian American, Gina leaned across the table and, filling acid into every syllable, said:

"How in the f___ does she ever put up with you?"

After breakfast came stretching, and with it the happy announcement that Carolyn's serial casting had done some good. While it was still difficult for her to move my shoulder, elbow, wrist, and fingers, the casting had at least made these movements possible without the sensation of cracking bones in half, so . . . no electrodes! *Yess!*

Gym was uneventful. Father Jim was in a snit over a TV ad for a car called the Millenia.

"You can't call a single object a 'Millennia,'" he was saying. "You have to call it 'Millennium' or it doesn't make any sense. You don't say, 'I'm buying a Pontiacs or a Fords,' do you, Peter? So how can you buy a Millenia?"

I told him I was not in the market for "a cars" this year, but either he didn't hear me or he was too busy making up his own joke. True to form, it was a musical one:

"Come away with me, Lucille," he crooned.
"In my merry Oldsmobiles."

To which he soon added:

"See the USA in your Chevrolets."

Vamping wildly, he tossed in skewed advertising lines, like:

"Put a Fords in your future."

and newer ones:

"See your Toyotas dealer today."

Father Jim was a real stickler, all right. On and on he went, griping about the fast-fading world he once knew, a world surrendered to "oafs, hooligans, and stumblebums" who have never opened a dictionary while our so-called modern lexicon set about to destroy the ordered, grammatically soothing language he once knew.

Our Boy Hadjo, also in the gym that morning, had been improving extraordinarily. Aside from his screams of pain that morning in the Room of Special Purpose, none of us had ever heard this polite, sweet-natured young man raise his voice. Today, however, he was fuming at his gym partner, Willie the Whiner, as they performed the "windshield wiper" leg exercise, the same exercise to which Father Jim usually had Ernie and me singing "If You Knew Susie" in rhythmic accompaniment. As the two lay on their backs, swinging clenched hands with stretched arms in opposite direction to legs that were locked at the knees with feet flat on the floor, Our Boy Hadjo was repeating, "You look at shirt."

This was in response to the question repeated interminably by the flat-voiced Willie, so that instead of the tuneful "If You Knew Susie," the gym was filled with doleful, monotonous repetitions of:

"Are you from China or Japan?"

"You look at shirt!"

"Are you from China or Japan?"

"You look at shirt!"

Willie simply could not grasp that there were, indeed, Oriental nations aside from the big two. So he repeated:

"Are you from China or Japan?"

Hadjo, meanwhile, his sense of chauvinism aroused, simply refused to cave in to this most annoying Occidental. His voice increased a few decibels with every repeat of:

"You look at shirt!"

Routine activities continued until, at the precise moment that a basketball was leaving Ernie's hands in what would normally be a perfect arc to a perfectly sunk basket, alarms and sirens began to blare throughout the building: the emergency evacuation drill!

Ernie, cursing as freely as if he were Gina, missed a basket for the first time, perhaps, since an oft-referred-to time back in grammar school when the Dodgers left Brooklyn and, for Ernie, all of life became meaningless.

To most of us, who, while thoroughly prepared for the drill, could not remember our Memory Books or where our own rooms were or how to get an outside phone line, the drill came as a complete surprise. What the hell was this? Fire? Air raid? Bombs planted in the locker room by the PLO?

Everyone was hustled into lines, various therapists and hospital personnel assuring us that there were no hidden bombs, no fires, no raids, and that this was merely a drill. This calmed and reassured all of us almost immediately. All of us, that is, except for Ernie, who at about the same time the Dodgers left Brooklyn, was also instructed by nuns to get under his desk during A-bomb drills and to cover himself with a white sheet brought from home, thus assuring that he could not possibly be harmed by radiation.

Ernie was three people ahead of me in line and I was last as we all marched quietly, ears open for directions. Turning a major corner, the four of us nearest the end accidentally became interlocked with another line of patients moving in the opposite direction. For the moment, it became impossible to tell which line one was supposed to be in. Those of us led by Ernie became cut off from our own main body and were soon lost and twisting in confusion. Reforming behind Ernie, we were spotted by the assistant physical therapist, Susan, who called to us. Ernie dutifully heeded while we three dutifully followed. However, in the midst of sirens, bells, and bodies swirling all around us, Ernie made an unexpected turn.

"Gotta get a sheet," he mumbled. "Part of the drill."

Clearly, the man was nuts. I would now prove that I was completely back to normal. What an opportunity—I would let everyone else go on and find my own way back to the main group!

Isn't this the way they turned? Yes, yes, I'm sure of it. But wait a minute, isn't that the closet where that big slop sink is? Let's check it out, just to get my bearings.

Opening the closet door, however, what did I find there in place of brooms, mops, cleansers, and a tub-sized sink? You guessed it—that big flashing neon sign reading "Easy Street"!

How did this get here? is what I thought, but "Oh, hell, I'll just go in" is what I said aloud. If I bumped into my group, I'd just pretend I knew they were here.

And I could report on Ernie and the other wanderers, showing a fitness to be sent home while saving them from unspeakable torture and death at the hands of Arafat's extremist minions.

Alas, my little gym group was not on Easy Street. Others, however, had wandered in. Among these was June Ann, the sweet elderly lady of the gnarled, arthritic hands. With her was a teenager, Jacqueline, an extremely corpulent newcomer who was standing at the window of Easy Street's bank, bawling loudly while dripping great globules of tears.

"It's all right, Jacqui, you'll be fine," June Ann cooed. "This is only a drill. It's practice."

Jacqueline, however, could not be soothed. She bawled loudly, wildly, pausing only to inhale huge, rasping gulps of oxygen as a half dozen rivulets explored new ways down the several layers of fatty deposits that made up her large, frightened face. Poor Jacqueline needed money to go to Elmira, New York, before the bombs started dropping, and she was terribly upset that there was no teller here on Easy Street to execute the transaction. My heart went out to the poor kid immediately, and I was on the verge of offering her the supply of tollbooth quarters Dad had given me when Georgette appeared and took control of the situation. Jacqueline, it seemed, had been in the care of a new male attendant who had escorted her to one of the handicapped ladies rooms, which is where she was when the alarm sounded. In the confusion, the girl sneaked out of the ladies room to get some money for Elmira. Nothing ever escaped Georgette, however. She was onto the case within seconds and was now soothing and mothering. Poor hog-jowled Jacqueline lapped it up, but pink-faced, white-haired Georgette reminded her of her grandmother, and so the kid just kept bawling and sobbing, only now it was for her grandma.

"Can't somebody shut that kid up?" I turned around. Willie the Whiner had wandered in. "For Christ's sake, they call this a drill?" he continued.

Georgette explained that the point of the exercise was to show any weak spots in the procedure and that information thus gathered would be applied toward improvement.

"Improvement!" Willie roared. "What's to improve? We've all just been incinerated!"

Jacqueline's discovery that she'd just been incinerated set her howling even more.

"Where's my grandma?" she wailed, miserable and confused. "I want to go home!"

As Georgette soothed and reassured Jacqueline, Charlie wandered in, attracted by the excitement that by now was making me feel extremely edgy. I told Georgette that I was about to have an anxiety attack.

"No, you are not," came the firm decree from the Vienna Woods. "You are a strong, capable man. People here may need your help."

That did it. "People here may need your help" instantly recalled every faded memory of what was expected of a good man, as learned from dear old Dad.

A good man was expected to flash his upbeams to warn passing motorists of road troubles he's just passed (but not of an imminent speed trap, which the other guy just might deserve).

A good man was expected to help motorists who were in trouble, to help a neighbor shovel his walk, to dig his car out of a snowbank, to help paint his house.

But a good man did not have anxiety attacks, certainly not in the face of all-out nuclear warfare with Saddam Hussein.

And I was a good man.

But I was also a boy who knew his apples, remember. I should have known that any anxiety was due less to imminent nuclear evaporation than to the sudden arrival of Charlie and what I knew he would pressure me to do.

Charlie, of course, had been speaking of escape since I first met him, and this was certain to be on his mind today, during all the confusion. He assured me, however, that he had discovered where the rest of my group was and that he merely wanted to lead me back to them. "Yeah, right, Charlie. Sure."

"No, no, I promise you, Jake, I know where they are, just up here."

But we had to get away from the howling, the snarling, and the bawling of Easy Street because he couldn't think straight.

"I've never led you wrong, and I won't start now, so come on. Trust me."

Here again, however, I steadfastly resolved to hold my ground as with every other important decision at Gaylord.

And then I followed him.

Georgette was preoccupied with Willie the Whiner and Jacqueline, and so did not notice me being led off by the bakery owner. On our way out we passed Eddie, the Fireman Who Barks Like a Dog. He was entering Easy Street and seemed as confused as I about where he should be and what he should be doing.

"Ignore him," Charlie said. "He's probably just looking for a fire hydrant."

The hallway outside Easy Street was a scene from *Night of the Living Dead,* filled with cadavers like me bumping into each other as they were led by staff to the safety of the outdoors.

"Where's our group?"

"Just up here."

"We'd better get out of here, Charlie."

"Trust me."

We were stopped by a staff assistant.

"You guys know where you're going?"

"Oh, yeah," said Charlie the Spokesman, pointing through the glass door where another group from our TBI unit had assembled.

"We're with that bunch."

Good old Charlie. Nutty as Aunt Anna's fruitcake but, man, could he think fast when breaking a rule.

He must have gone to Catholic school.

But it didn't work. The attendant led us outside and told the therapist in charge to keep an eye on us while he located our real unit. Eddie, who was on another evacuation line by now, had apparently been transgressed by some poor, unsuspecting patient, because he chose that particular moment to release one of his more outstanding howls. Charlie suddenly froze in rigid attention, and his head jerked toward the sound. I asked if he was all right.

"Shh!" he ordered. "There it is!"

"There *what* is?"

"The snow leopard. He's calling!"

"Charlie, that's not an animal, that's—"

But just then another of Eddie's howls filled the warm morning air.

"That's it! Come on, Desi, we're outta here!"

With that, good old Charlie broke the line, getting only about seven or eight feet away before being stopped by an attendant who, as he argued with Charlie, reminded him that if necessary he would be restrained with a posie. This, of course, would apply to the rest of Charlie's henchmen, I figured.

That was it! No one was going to get me into a posie any more than they were going to stuff the subcutaneous tissue of my left hand full of anodes and cathodes.

I was out of this joint!

Having made this irrevocable decision, I walked, not ran, in the direction of my room, determined to pack my things and simply inform the nurse at the desk that I was well enough to leave and was checking myself out.

Thus determined, I strode manfully across one of Gaylord's

many outdoor terraces, planning what I was about to say over the phone to my wife, my darling, my Mary Michael, knowing I would need either her or dear old Dad to drop everything, drive across Long Island, take that long ferry ride (impossible, really, without a reservation), then drive up the Connecticut coast to Gaylord. Thus bristling with plans and energy, I slammed directly into my friend Jack, the social therapist.

Jack led me to a quiet bench, listened to all my concerns, then asked me to consider the upset this would cause my wife and family. Hadn't they been through enough?

Jack really knew how to press my buttons, all right. Even with a broken-down brain, how could anyone argue against the option of not hurting one's family?

Certainly not a boy who knew his apples.

10

Closing Ceremonies

June 13, 1992. I asked Joan, whom Ernie sometimes calls "the school shrink," why I now have this tendency to become emotional over the slightest things. As a man of the nineties, of course, I should know that crying can be a good thing, something men might permit more often.

Mary Michael, unlike me, has always been a great crier. Oh, she cries at the usual things: weddings, funerals, Frank Capra endings. But she also cries at marching bands, at carousels, at your average, everyday set of bagpipes playing "Danny Boy" or "Amazing Grace."

Mary Michael would cry at a supermarket opening.

I cried when I learned that Mike died and when I'd been daydreaming about being with my wife, only to come up with a handful of Ernie's rotten, ant-covered Chunky bar. But before that, I'd shed nary a tear since age eleven or so when our dog Stumpy (don't ask) had to be put down.

Now my own little Mississippi not only overflowed with regularity, but often threw in a Nile, an Amazon, and a couple of spouting Old Faithfuls for good measure.

"It's not just normal flooding, either," I complained. "It's monsoons. It's February in Seattle, rainy season in India. What's going on?"

"You realize that emotions may be affected by a brain injury, don't you?" Joan asked.

"To this extent?"

"Does that disturb you?"

"Sometimes it feels pretty good."

"Then don't knock it."

Okay. So now, in addition to being a Man Who Can't Tell Which Day Is Friday and a Man Who Can't Find His Own Room and a Man Who Can't Tie His Own Sneakers, I would be a Man Who Cries.

The way one gets through such strange new discoveries about oneself is the same way one gets through the inability to walk, think properly, or tie one's own sneakers. What one keeps telling oneself is something quite like what Sister Attila Marie might have said:

It could have been worse.

Strange, isn't it, that no matter how miserable we may be, we draw this sadistic comfort from the knowledge that out there somewhere, perhaps on the steppes of Central Asia or in Moscow's central ward or in South L.A., someone is even more miserable than we are? What kind of creatures are we?

Of course, in my case, the only logical alternative to my present way of life was death, a concept that no longer frightened me because of certain adventures in that realm, a realm I visited but which we have not yet discussed.

"There's a reason for this," Mike is said to have told Mary Michael when he first learned of my injury. Unfortunately, he never mentioned what that reason might be.

And I didn't have a great deal of time to think about those reasons, since Gaylord's hectic schedule never provided a moment for reflection. Alone in bed at night, though, I might think of my brave, hard-working wife and kids or of my simple, loving parents who each day taught the lesson of giving. Tears would pour.

There might be a news story about some child paraplegic who made it through college at age six. Tears would pour.

About some little ones saved from a fire. Ditto.

About a homeless old woman, a little boy being a kidney donor, a kitten up a tree: ditto, ditto, ditto.

Memories of personal kindnesses shown to me in the past suddenly flooded my brain for no apparent reason, triggering the most tears. Some of these generosities dated back to my television writing days and were committed by those who seemed to be the most unlikely people.

Most celebrities know and recognize each other and are gracious, outgoing, and courteous to those who accompany them. *What pressure to be a celebrity,* I remember thinking in those days. *You're always on. And everybody always loves you, or so they say.* In the case of my friends Jerry Stiller and Anne Meara, though, it was true that everybody loved them. With good reason.

Consider that this hilarious husband-and-wife comedy team first achieved national fame through appearances on *The Ed Sullivan Show* throughout the late fifties and early sixties. Sullivan, of course, had been responsible for the success of many whom we all know and love today.

When Sullivan died, it was anticipated that the Campbell

Funeral Home, where New York's wealthy and famous go when they die, would be overflowing with those whose careers had been "made" by Ed.

If you had gone there with a camera and an autograph book, however, you would have been largely disappointed. No Beatles. No Supremes. No world-famous stand-up comics, singers, jugglers, acrobats, or pop stars. They were too busy tending the careers that had been so lavishly boosted by appearances on Sullivan's show. They were too busy, that is, except for that funny, funny Jewish guy from East New York and that funny, funny Irish Catholic wife of his from Long Island: Jerry Stiller and Anne Meara.

I, myself, have written for a number of famous actors, singers, and comics. I also came to know dozens of fellow writers, producers, directors, publicity people, journalists, and editors. As I lay on what nearly became my death bed, however, only two of them aside from my close Westhampton friends thought to call me. The thoughtful two?

Jerry Stiller and Anne Meara.

Later, when home in Westhampton, Anne would again call with house seats for Mary Michael and me to attend the Broadway production of O'Neill's *Anna Christie*, in which Anne was appearing with Liam Neeson and Natasha Richardson. And when her own work, *Afterplay*, debuted off Broadway, Anne's assistant called with another two house seats to be used at our convenience.

In the 1970s, I wrote a TV pilot, *Heartaches*, for them. In one of those zigs just before a zag in one's writing career, it turned out that the CBS executive who was to give final approval of this comedy about a man and his heart attack was himself in the hospital recovering from—you guessed it—a heart attack. He did not find the subject amusing.

The pilot went no further. Jerry and Anne felt terrible, mostly for a certain young writer with mouths to feed who had devoted weeks of labor to the project without wages. Soon, they issued an off-the-cuff invitation for me, my wife, and our two kids to join them for a week at their new vacation home on Nantucket. There, we were thoroughly wined and dined, treated like visiting shahs, and never permitted to shell out a single dollar.

On the ferry back to the mainland, I discovered what Jerry had shoved into my pocket as we were leaving—a check in an amount close to what I would have received had our deal gone through.

Like my dear friend Mike, Anne and Jerry were both true *mensches*.

And Old Faithful blew again.

What would I be like at home for Matt's graduation? Would this lack of control embarrass my wife? my kids? my family? my community? my country? Was I hopeless?

The graduation celebration was, by this time, shaping into much more than a family rite of passage. A number of people whom I hadn't seen for the months during my hospitalization would attend, so Mary Michael conned Matt into permitting his day to be partly mine by okaying the invitation of many, many friends.

Hearing of this act of generosity on my son's special day, I did what any other red-blooded American male would do: I cried.

Walking was not quite routine yet; I still needed the wheelchair for longer jaunts. That meant I would go home in Dad's van, and upon recalling that he'd bought it specifically to transport yours truly in the event that I might never walk again, what do you think I did? I cried.

The day came when my family arrived to bring me home for Matt's graduation. As we drove down the leafy road away from Gaylord, the institution that had shown me how to be a human being again, my darling wife slid her hand into mine. I cried.

As we crossed Long Island Sound on the ferry, I felt that a new life lay ahead even though my time at Gaylord was not yet through. I cried.

Then, on the trek across Long Island, Mary Michael spoke of the many great kindnesses performed on our behalf by the good people of Westhampton: of the lifts to the ferry; of the several weeks of dinners delivered hot and fresh every night; of the assistance with our overwhelming hospital bills; of lawn people and pool people and lawyers and even the dry cleaner absolutely refusing payment. I cried.

Finally, as we passed the old mill on the Montauk Highway and near it, a little green sign, I had to grab a handkerchief. My Mississippi-Amazon-Nile-Old Faithful combo, fully primed, threatened to drown one and all as I turned, in my own mind, into a bawling, sobbing, babbling wretch.

What did that little green area sign say?

Westhampton.

* * *

The day of my son's graduation was nothing if not triumphal. The weather was beautiful, and so the ceremony was held outdoors in the football stadium, where my entry with Mary Michael and with a cane (but no wheelchair!) was greeted by what seemed like hundreds of well-wishers from my adopted hometown of Westhampton Beach, Long Island, my pretty little coastal village of some 1,600, which inflated each summer to some 20,000 with the arrival of tourist season.

In Westhampton Beach, old-timers like me might easily be well acquainted with any number of the town's residents, including many writers, composers, and actors. We might also be on a first-name basis with every bank president, all three school principals, the entire village board, the police chief, the fire chief, all of the priests and ministers and the single rabbi, and each of the forty or so Main Street shopkeepers as well as the local mortician, who, in a unique indication of just how much this remains small-town America, also happens to be the president of the chamber of commerce.

These were the people who had performed the most extraordinary acts of kindness for my wife and family when I became ill, and many of them were now on hand, waving and beaming in genuine happiness to see me enter the sunshine of this very small, very typical high school arena with Mary Michael at my side.

I had received my bronze, my silver, and my gold medals for various events on that long road from darkness and confusion into this bright yellow day. Today, I was triumphantly entering the sunny Olympic stadium with my loving wife, walking with a cane, but otherwise on my own before what surely must have been at least a hundred thousand spectators, with hundreds of millions picking up the glorious closing ceremonies on cable feeds and satellite dishes around the globe. By the time Matt proceeded in with the class of 1992 I was blubbering and wheezing like Dad's old 1949 slope-back Pontiac.

More tears fell at the graduation party that followed at the waterfront home of Sunny Miller, who had become terribly close to us since the death of her husband, my old buddy Mike of the bottomless heart and basset hound face.

I nearly cried again upon learning that some of the celebrities I've worked with were also affected by my illness. Jay Leno's reaction, in particular, touched me deeply because I had been so impressed with his character when we met in 1991.

He took over *The Tonight Show* during my months at

Gaylord. Apparently pleased by my article, he requested another interview with *Parade.* Dotson, who handled it in my absence, said that Leno's first comments were words of concern about my health. You can believe he was sincere.

Leno lives far up in the Hollywood Hills in a large house where he and his wife, Mavis, lead as uncluttered a life as your Uncle Jake. It is reached via what seems an endlessly snaking road veering up, up, up until, finally, you reach his gate and then, when you are admitted, you go down, down, down, stopping at a large parking area.

On the day I arrived for my *Parade* interview, he was nowhere in sight. Finally calling out, I heard his reedy voice shout back, "I'm in here, Pete—just a sec!"

With this he appeared at a small window, baseball cap on backward, in a sweat-stained Harley-Davidson T-shirt and with a wrench in his hand, instructing me to come through the front door, which was open.

Most Hollywood (and New York) interviews involve, if not servants, then at least a press agent or two, but not so with Leno.

Leno works alone.

At the time he had replaced Joan Rivers as Johnny Carson's substitute host on *The Tonight Show,* and was already presumed to be taking over the show upon Carson's approaching retirement.

Leno also avoids pretense, a feeling he must have sensed that I share since he had no difficulty asking me to move the washing machine he was in the midst of fixing. Together, we pulled it away from the wall so he could get behind it with that wrench.

"Sorry to ask you, Pete," he said unself-consciously, "But you live in a place like this, who you gonna ask, Jack Lemmon?"

Lemmon, it turned out, lived directly next door, a fact that interested Leno but with which he was not, nor could he ever be, impressed to the point of self-inflation. Lemmon was a good guy, a fine actor, a decent neighbor. Leno? He minded his own business.

He was a man who cooked his own lunch, made his own travel arrangements, carried his own luggage, fixed his own washing machine, wrote his own jokes. On a terrace looking out on those Hollywood Hills, he told me his basic philosophy. I'd asked him if he did much swimming, indicating the large and beautiful pool.

"Nah," he told me. "The only time I'm in that thing is when I'm adjusting the main drain or clearing out the returns. When I've earned it, maybe I'll give myself a little break."

He took me to one of his three garages, one of which had two levels, to show me the rewards he does permit himself: his indulgence in cars and motorcycles.

"These are my babies," he said. "But I don't buy one until I feel I've earned it." And he earns them by working hard.

On a legal pad in his living room were the beginnings of the monologue with which he would begin that day's taping at about 6:00 P.M. The one note I glimpsed never made it into full joke form and was not used, but the skewed association of two jotted-down concepts showed how his comedic mind works: "Tammy Faye Bakker" was written on one side of the page, with the then-newsworthy name joined by a line to the punch phrase, "Sears Weatherbeater Makeup."

The happiness of the graduation party, the pride in my son and daughter, the warmth of friends and comfort of family all confirmed a fact I had really known for some time by this point: I was not insane, but, like many another brain-injured person, I had difficulty in discovering, and then accepting, reality. After the party I returned to Gaylord but was permitted weekends away as a way of easing the return of self-sufficiency. These weekends were spent at Ledgeway, the estate of my beautiful Aunt Florence in nearby Redding Ridge, Connecticut. Soon I returned, fully prepared and without fanfare, to my little town of Westhampton.

Mom and Dad had retired to a small town nearby, and Dad often came by for real, not imaginary, walks with Spike. Dad, never one to withhold his passion or his opinion, was as full of vinegar as ever.

"I just don't get what anyone has against your Jews," he said on one occasion after watching a New York newscast about a Jewish cemetery that had been desecrated with swastikas and hate words. "My God, what'd them people ever do to us?" he asked rhetorically. "Just look at all the good Jews you got in this world," he said, naming Jessel, Burns, Cantor, and a host of show biz folk including my old Uncle Milton. I never did tell Dad about our personal encounter, on the grounds that he may have thought Berle indecent.

"What'd them people ever do to us?" he repeated with uncommon passion.

As devil's advocate, I reminded him that those who tend to be clannish, even for self-protection, are automatically suspect in the eyes of others. He wasn't buying.

"What about the Polacks?" he said, reminding me of my own partially Polish heritage, and that the Poles had banded together to form a near-private enclave in our own little corner of Ozone Park. "Nobody bothers us!" I didn't have the nerve to remind him of Polish jokes and certainly not of the outrageous put-downs, some of them quite stinging, which one may hear to this day among the local wealthy, educated, and otherwise sophisticated summer residents, particularly the self-appointed grandees of Southampton.

"What about Chinatown?" Dad continued. "And Little Italy? Don't them people stick together?"

I had to play my trump card.

"People still say it was the Jews who killed Christ, you know."

"Bull!" he shot back. "Jesus was put out by his own, that's the whole idea. If he was born in Holland, does that mean you're supposed to hate the Dutch?"

Dad, I realized, was more sophisticated than I ever knew.

And more loving. In bed that night, I recalled Mary Michael's description of how he had been seen at my bedside a year earlier, eyes glistening with emotion as he murmured words meant only for his son, who was deep in a coma and, at that moment, close to death. I finally realized that, his own youthful error with his little boy aside, here was a man who is as loving and as rock-solid as they come, a man from whom the great self-ordained sophisticates of Southampton or any other earthbound spot might take a lesson; a powerful, muscular man, gentle as a calf and more thoughtful, more considerate, more downright loving than any other I have met. He is a man who, in this era of men routinely saying "I love you" to other men without necessarily meaning it, has never had to say "I love you" to me. I have always known it.

That night, I reached down very, very deep to seek and wipe out any vestiges of resentment I might have had against my father for having inadvertently created that little boy who couldn't throw a ball.

But I sure as hell didn't find any.

11

A Little Omphaloskepsis Can Go a Long Way

> *January 28, 1993*. Being faithful to my journal is the only way I'll get back to writing, so it's time to start.

With that simple statement I resumed my craft, devoting hours each day to a journal I hoped eventually to use as the basis for a book. By this point, I'd been out of Gaylord more than four months, spending my days at a center for therapy cleverly named the Center for Therapy. An invalid coach would faithfully pick me up with my lunch bag and my dollar for soda each morning at eight o'clock, dropping me off again at around four o'clock.

Sensing that all this therapy business was becoming a drag, my Aunt Florence, who is only a few years older than I am, provided me with a two-week vacation at her winter condo on the beach in Delray Beach, Florida, all expenses paid. With her estate in Connecticut, her loft in New York's Soho district, and this winter haven on the ocean, Florence had come a long way, indeed, since the days when my father and his stepbrothers, Eddie and Freddie, pushed her around Ozone Park in a coal-filled baby carriage.

Family lore had it that Florence's arrival had come as quite a surprise to my grandfather, then in his sixties and my step-grandmother, who was around fifty. It was Florence who possessed, in our family, the uncontested title of "black sheep."

Uncontested? Hell, with her foul mouth, her love of boys' games, her stunningly ribald stories, her eagerness to thumb her nose at convention, her ability to remain unfazed and unhurt by mere words (and back in the old, convention-bound Ozone Park of the 1950s, there were a lot of "mere words"), she was not just anyone's black sheep.

She was the Mother of All Black Sheep.

She married young to a sturdy, reliable Ozone Park kind of guy who could not have been fully aware of the whirlwind that she was. She and Vinnie had an amicable divorce, and she married her business partner, Brian Mahony, years later.

With Brian, Florence entered the booming Manhattan employment agency industry of the 1960s. They began with a single agency that, with their combined talents, soon grew to eighteen. To their relationship, Brian brought education and logic, cool, calm reasoning, and a passion for fairness. Florence brought compassion, dynamic enthusiasm, a love of hard work, the same passion for fairness, and an undying sense of outrageous, often bawdy, humor (many an iffy business deal was saved when a difficult and intractable client found himself collapsed in laughter at one of her wildly unconventional and hilarious remarks). Together, Brian and Florence worked magic.

And they made a fortune. To this day, they lead a good, comfortable life filled with travel and adventure, but one in which "things" are virtually meaningless. People count. Deeds count. Giving others an opportunity counts most of all.

And my family and I counted when we were in our deepest, deepest woes. When we lost our house, our investments, our life's savings, Flo and Brian were there to be sure that Mary Michael and I, and our kids, never quite fell apart. My sister, Pat, or my parents, I know, would have done the same had they the resources. And they did respond most importantly with bottomless reserves of love, goodwill, and moral support, not only for me but also for my wife and children. What is surprising about Flo and Brian, though, is that they did not merely have the resources: They had the will to be there for us. Damned if they'd let my little family wither.

And we didn't.

January 29, 1993, Delray Beach, 4:00 A.M. One task while I'm here is to run across Route A1A each morning to pick up a *New York Times* from one of those machines that people around here seem to prefer to corner newspaper stands operated by the blind. Actually, *run* is hardly the word, since my left leg really isn't all that strong and tends to drag behind me.

So what I really do is this: I slog.

That's how trim, athletic Brian refers to my little task of picking up the *Times:* going out for my "morning slog."

When I return, he will invariably have prepared a healthy breakfast for all of us consisting, first, of some bizarre health liquid that smells like pond scum and looks like drained brake fluid, with a taste and viscosity to match both. This is followed by freshly squeezed (if not pitted) orange or grapefruit juice and then a bowl of grains that would feed Iowa, topped with freshly made yogurt and garnished with a generous portion of slices from some as-yet-unnamed species of fruit.

By breakfast I would already have been at work for several hours. Brian and Flo could not understand why I rose so early to work when the whole purpose of being here was to relax and gather after a long physical and mental struggle. At the same time they, and others, wondered why I seemed more devoted to writing and less devoted to exercises that might help restore some hint of motion to the still-dead left hand.

My answer was that just as a professional running back must concentrate on the restoration of a damaged knee, a writer must concentrate on the restoration of a damaged brain.

Each morning, then, I would rise with the sun to enter a room that in the state of New York is called a "Florida room," but in the state of Florida is called what it's called in the state of Hawaii: a lanai. There, with the sun barely blinking over a cinemascopic view of the Atlantic as clouds dispelled, stiff shards of yellow breaking up the gray predawn murk, and sea birds plummeting and diving, one had the distinct feeling of walking directly into a gigantic picture postcard.

Of course, the material I wrote, while no longer gibberish, was hardly the polished prose desired. But the mere act of churning out five or six handwritten sheets on a legal pad helped me remember what it is that a writer does: He writes.

* * *

Omphaloskepsis is hardly a word used, say, at the garage or down at the mall or even on *Jeopardy,* so I'll save at least some of you a trip to the dictionary:

It is the contemplation of one's omphalos, or navel, as a connective thread linking all of humanity back generation before generation until we arrive at either Mother Eve and the glorious world of creation or a couple of horny apes on the Serengeti, depending upon one's persuasion. (My vote, for the record, is for the apes and no, this does not interfere with acceptance of the Bible, which may have been inspired by the divine but whose poetic language came from men.)

Omphaloskepsis is used here in its more common reference, that is, as the simple act of looking inward while attempting to understand one's own life if not life itself. It was in this sense that I peered into my omphalos more and more as my daily slogs grew longer and longer. My goal soon became a little public park about a half mile north of Flo and Brian's home, where I would sit, gazing at the ol' omphalos, trying to figure out just what in hell had happened when I'd entered that bizarre but very real and loving world of the spirit almost a year earlier.

Gazing at the sea from among breezy palms, an occasional lizard flitting across the path in that little park, I got to know my omphalos a little bit better (mine is an "innie"). Eventually, instead of randomly floating memories, the spiritual events of a year earlier finally assembled themselves in a logical progression. Now I could see that, as I turned to prayer while slipping slowly off that chair and into what I thought would be nothingness, I entered the strange and wondrous world that awaits all of us. But let me preface my report with a disclaimer or two.

First, this experience was so powerful and compelling to me that I cannot possibly convey the sense of awe, of power, of majesty it evoked—and still does every day.

Second, I worry that its retelling will place this entire work into the "NDE" category, there being so many works on the near-death experience that it now has its own argot in the publishing trade. I don't knock NDE literature. Anyone who comes in contact with his or her spiritual self, in whatever manner, is a richer, fuller, happier human. However, I find it more important to report this experience as the remarkable conversion it represented—that of an atheist *within the context of his seriously damaged brain.*

But consider this: If you have read this far, you already know a good deal about that damaged brain and of the effects of TBI in general. You have met many of the characters I came to know at Gaylord, and you have observed their behavior through this author's own particular, albeit broken, prism. You will undoubtedly recall that for many months I was haunted by "memory snatches" of my "other world" experience. These occurred unannounced throughout the healing process, but my brain was not strong enough at those points to pull them together or to understand what actually happened. In short, I knew that each of those memory snatches represented something true, something that actually occurred, but I could not put any of it into a coherent whole.

It is ironic that the following story—which will sound to some like it's being told from the Cuckoo's Nest—was actually the sign, I realized much later, of a *healing* brain that was finally well enough to sort its memories into logical order. Makes sense. The old brain, coming back into practice again because of all the writing I had forced upon it, was well enough at last to begin piecing events together.

A lot of you won't believe my experience, which is fine. If you'd told me such a story before it happened to me, I'd have hooted you out of the room. But this is what I now most clearly recall, moment by moment, as I slipped off my "secure" living room chair and into a world whose existence I'd so vehemently denied.

* * *

"Our Father who art in heaven,"

came the prayer dredged from childhood at the last moment of panic.

"hallowed be thy name."

Where's this coming from? I remember thinking, but all that mattered was to keep going.

"Thy kingdom come.
Thy will be done on earth, as it is in heaven."

Some things you just don't forget, I guess. Like riding a bicycle. Sure is a perfect prayer.

"Give us this day our daily bread,"

My daily bread, my daily bread. Well, obviously what I need now is to be sure my kids don't find me dead. So don't let me die, not yet, that'll be my daily bread for today. Okay?

"and forgive us our trespasses,
as we forgive those who trespass against us,"

God? God, if you're really there, have I ever done you wrong! I'm sorry. And I really do forgive all those people who messed me up. They didn't know what they were doing.

"and lead us not into temptation,"

What could tempt me now? Despair, maybe? No way, not when I'm just beginning to feel there's someone there and I'm about to find out.

"but deliver us from evil."

Yes, yes! If there is evil where I'm going, try to remember I wasn't such a bad guy.

"Amen."

So be it. I was becoming what the doughboys of World War I called a "foxhole Christian," and I knew it.

To be honest, I don't know whether I got through the entire prayer, but I was fervently sincere (as one might imagine!) and I do recall the warm, comfortable feeling of this prayer on my lips as I slid down, down, down into what looked like our living room carpet but would actually be a real, live brush with eternity, if there was such a thing.

This is it, came another thought I can still remember quite clearly. *You're about to find out.* Though it doesn't seem possible, I actually felt a sense of adventure and daring. I was like a little boy in Coney Island's old Steeplechase Park, just beginning the breathless descent down those giant, polished wooden slides in the indoor pavilion. This was a slow, slow ride, however, and there was plenty of time to think about what was at the bottom. Would there be some long-deceased relative waiting to catch me? Would there be a white light? Would there be a tunnel? Whatever would happen, I felt safe, but curious and excited. If there were no God and no eternity, there would be nothingness. Simple as that.

But there wasn't nothingness.

There was no white light, either.

And no tunnel.

And no ethereal space. No skylike travel. No clouds. No Jesus. No Virgin. No saints. No long-gone Yankee grandma or Aunt Anna or anyone else sweetly beckoning.

Not for me.

I simply emerged (without knowing how) into what seemed a large, rectangular room populated with people, or other souls—beings, at any rate, who were identifiable as other humans. No wings, no halos, no harps. No Botticelli there. They were all human in appearance and all quite beautiful. Don't think Hollywood. Don't think TV. Don't think or trust any depiction of this phenomenon you may have seen.

It's not like that. Or it wasn't for me.

What these beings had in common was that they were peaceful. They were calm. And they were very, very beautiful. Each one glowed with a mysterious light that came from within, the way a lamp shade appears when the bulb is turned on. I wanted to move among them, but I needed a moment to acclimate, one of several surprisingly "human" feelings that would remain. I glanced through the crowd, recognizing no one. No one recognized me. I had another surprisingly earthbound thought: There had been no deaths in my family in quite some time, so how would I know anyone?

I understood innately that this was a way station of some sort, a place where souls or shades gathered before moving on to somewhere else. Was I in limbo? It didn't matter. I was fine.

What calm, I thought. *What tranquillity. Everyone is perfectly happy, perfectly content and at ease.* The notion of being dead was not disturbing, although it was by no means certain that dead is what I was.

If this was death, well, fine. It was good to be here. No harm can come to anyone here, I knew. No pain. No anxieties or worries. No desires. Only peace, contentment, love. Love on the most extraordinary level. Deep love, all-pervasive love. A love I'd never known could exist.

Is everyone really dead? Am I really dead? What's this all about? What's going on here?

Entrance into this world, I realized or was somehow told, was simply a human version of metamorphosis as we move from one level of being to another. Maggots cast off their wormlike selves to become houseflies. Caterpillars cast off their cocoons to become butterflies. People cast off their earthbound bodies to become finer spirits in another dimension. It's a continuum.

All made perfect sense.

I had received this information innately and would receive, it was now clear, more such innate information, simply by wanting it.

Yet the answer to the biggest question—whether I was dead—was ambiguous. At this point, death was fine with me. Even my deepest concern—that of Matthew and Emily Kate finding my body on the living room floor when they got home from school—could no longer trouble me as it had when I was struggling to hold on to life. Now there was nothing that could be troubling. Nothing.

Am I smiling? I must be—everyone else is. Who wouldn't smile?

I wanted to walk through this space. To know it. To possess it. I began to move.

I'm moving, but I'm not walking. What is this? Am I floating? Am I gliding?

This was a totally effortless form of locomotion neither you nor I have ever known, and it can't be adequately described. *Floating* and *gliding* come closest.

I'm a spirit—I really, really am a spirit! Not like Casper. Not like Patrick Swayze in *Ghost.* Not like anything in the Bible or catechisms or Dante or Milton. Not like anything that can be described.

And I'm perfectly calm, perfectly happy and at peace. But I want to know: Why am I here? Do I deserve this? I don't think so.

Another earthbound realization was that I had not caused my own depression and could, therefore, now be free of any related guilt. Furthermore, any notion of sin needed to be thought of not in terms of Charlton Heston yelling from a mountaintop but of Jesus, himself, giving us the two Great Commandments: to love God with our whole minds and our whole hearts and our whole souls; and to love our neighbors as ourselves.

This is it! came the wonderful realization. *This is exactly what it's all about! What everything's about! If I haven't sinned by all I've done to my wife and family, who has sinned? Has Dotson?*

My good friend Dotson came to mind for two reasons, I later realized:

One is that at the time of my collapse, he had been shortly due to arrive for work on our joint film project and had, therefore, been present in my subconscious.

The other is that I had long wondered how he could justify his being a fully practicing Roman Catholic with also being an avowed and outspoken homosexual.

Dotson, like any gay person, it became known to me, did not choose his orientation but had had it imposed on him either biologically or psychologically. Dotson was guiltless. If he has otherwise committed no harm, he is as worthy and deserving as any other human being and will find his own way to this place, or something like it.

The concept of sin as it existed here seemed very different from the concept of sin as it existed on earth. When I was a child, taught by nuns, brothers, and later by priests at the University of Dayton, there were very grave notions of good and evil, reward and punishment. We were still, it is now possible to see, in the very final stages of an Old Testament way of thinking.

Perhaps it had been necessary for the Old Testament to rely on fear and fire and brimstone. People were even more unruly then, and even less sophisticated.

Now, after thousands of years, after great wars, after great philosophers and scientists, and after having digested the wares of Freud and Jung, the human race may be prepared to examine the concept that the reality of heaven and hell lies within each one of us; that the seat of the soul, sought for centuries, is actually the unconscious mind; and that it is the unconscious mind that exists for eternity. We, therefore, live forever with the knowledge of the good or ill we have done; hence we carry our own individual heavens and hells within us. This could be the very interpretation of the "many mansions" of which Jesus tells us.

I'm no theologian and have no plans to become one, but maybe, just maybe, these thoughts are correct, or close to it.

One notion, at least, became incontrovertibly clear during my period in this gorgeous and exciting environment. It is that we aren't merely expected to avoid doing evil; we are expected to do good. And how can we best do that?

"It's easy," the Beatles sang, and they had it exactly right:

"All you need is love."

The room was filled with other shades, a term I have borrowed from Dante because *spirit* doesn't seem quite right. Interestingly, neither these shades nor I seemed to match any preconception of the word *ethereal.* Except for the intense and beautiful light glowing from within, the shades seemed quite like human beings as we all know them, with just one major difference: They were all so happy.

Some appeared to be seated, though it was hard to imagine any need for rest. Passing by a piece of furniture, I deliberately ran a hand against it, knowing it would pass through, yet needing to experiment. The hand passed. Sure, a similar incident occurred in the movie *Ghost.* It is possible that this, and other, elements were sprung from the subconscious; yet this can also be taken to support the notion that the subconscious may be the seat of the soul.

My interpretations, of course, are entirely subjective. Also remember, as I said, that I am not a psychiatrist, psychologist, philosopher, or theologian. I am simply a tourist and traveler trying to make sense of a previously undreamed-of world that was entered by chance. Some of you will interpret these adventures differently. Many of you will doubt them. This is fine. All I can do is remind you of something I said earlier:

I was there.

That notion, in my own mind, is irrefutable.

And remember, I know the arguments about psychological predilection and early childhood input and endorphins. I also remember what I used to say about Thomas Aquinas and his most referred-to proof for the existence of God. You know the one, about the Prime Mover, the proof that says if you trace everything and everyone back through the history of time, you have to come to the one Prime Mover, the cause of all motion and life, and we call that Prime Mover *God.*

Well, I might have asked Sister Attila Marie or my wife or her mother or my old Yankee grandma, or anyone in the theology department at the University of Dayton, why don't we just call it the Big Bang, the concept that is an atheist's best friend when discussing the origins of the universe. This was the notion I had accepted ever since I was nineteen and, like most other teenagers, discovered that I did, in fact, actually know everything. There was no God, I knew then, and therefore no cognitive, willful act of creation. There was just this bunch of chemicals, this volatile cosmic soup that always existed in the same way people said that God always existed until bang! The volatility reached overload. Chemical interaction induced life through sheer accident, thus blowing all of us into eventual existence, and so here we are. Why did we have to say it was a God who always existed when we've got this perfectly delicious chemical soup to account for us? Now I knew, though, that this was nonsense and that we did, indeed, have a loving God.

Unfortunately, though, memories of discovering, instead of being available, were locked within my own damaged and troubled brain, loose and ill-formed until they could at last be brought together as my mind, my thinking processes, and my memory slowly grew healthier.

While still in that space, or in that dimension that defies a term, I experienced a human curiosity about all those other shades, a mild interest in knowing who they were and what they were doing there. Yet I felt no need to speak, and so I didn't: All would become clear without asking, I knew. No one else showed a need or desire to communicate, either.

The space seemed large but vaguely defined: walls, furniture, a series of windows through which one could see some form of outdoors—peaceful, lovely, inviting, and suffused with a gorgeous yellow light.

That's it, that's Paradise, I suspected, surprised and happy to see that it really did appear to be a garden. Yet there was no way out there, not for me, not yet.

Is this what everyone's waiting for? To go into the region we have been taught is Paradise?

The answer was yes, though gaining access was not simply a matter of going out. Instead, I became aware of a series of alcoves within this large room. The room reminded me of the interior of our little Westhampton train station, a notion that made me suspect I was dreaming.

But I wasn't. There was a feeling, the very real presence of being in that space and *knowing* I was in the spiritual realm. Other dreams have seemed real, but this awareness, this *knowing* was quite new and quite beyond any doubt. To me, therefore, this was—and remains—real. No doubt, not yours or anyone's, can change this conviction. I was there, you see. One day you will be too.

The notion of a train station was compounded by the fact that all my fellow shades, like me, appeared to be waiting for something.

What is it? What's going to happen? With the thought barely realized, I knew that some decision would soon be reached, but that I was not to worry. My thoughts were fully active. So was my sense of confrontation and doubt.

Okay, if this is real, where's Jesus?

I think of this now and laugh at myself: a journalist quite literally to the end.

* * *

As these events were occurring in a spiritual realm, I felt no concern about my physical body, which was deep in a coma and quite close to death, the center of its own swirl of activity:

Arriving shortly after our phone conversation, Bertel Bruun discovered my comatose body on the floor near the chair in which he had instructed me to wait and from which I had by then fallen.

Recognizing the signs of a wildly hemorrhaging brain from years of neurological practice, Bertel diagnosed instantly. He knew that the subsequent blood clot, growing rapidly with the blood flow, was quite well advanced and that there was precious little time. Vital signs were weak, pulse barely perceptible. He took care of on-site emergency procedures, oversaw the emergency team that soon arrived, then attended me to our local country hospital.

The team at Central Suffolk Hospital, unequipped for brain surgery, had me stabilized and then moved to a more complete facility "up island" at Stony Brook University Hospital. Bertel called his wife, Ruth, telling her this was one of the most severe hemorrhages he'd seen in his years of practice. She asked the prognosis.

"I'm afraid you and I have seen Peter for the last time," he told her. He returned to my house where, with Mike, he awaited my wife and kids.

Mary Michael, by early afternoon, was returning from an appointment sitting in the passenger seat of her partner Norene's silver-gray Volvo. Mary Michael had recently seen her husband through the howling maw of depression; in twenty-four years of marriage she had seen his glowing reviews and bright promise as a playwright fade and then disappear as, with two young children, he turned to television for the handsome income it provided; the prolonged writers strike then tripped the depression. Now he was on the mend, but he could slip again.

At the same time, Mary Michael's son was facing high school graduation and college this year. Daughter Emily Kate was not far behind. Life since the strike had hardly been what she'd envisioned for herself and her family. Still, it was her job to somehow pull the kids together, hopefully helping them onto the track of a more secure, less pressured life for themselves. That late afternoon, it was time for her to pull over, find a pay phone, and check on her little family.

Mike answered the phone.

What's Mike doing there? she thought in surprise, recalling that it was Dotson with whom Peter was to work that day. But Mary Michael was even more surprised to learn, when he took the phone from Mike, that Bertel was also there.

"Something has happened," Bertel said in his light Danish accent. "You must come home immediately."

"What is it? What's going on?" Mary Michael asked, tinges of panic already settling into her voice.

"I cannot tell you. Just come directly home," Bertel insisted.

Mary Michael climbed back into Norene's Volvo, unable to say what happened but hoping against hope that her family was all safe.

As Mary Michael and Norene sped east, a MedEvac helicopter high above them sliced its way west. It seemed like any other helicopter, except this one contained the body of her stricken husband, being taken to immediate brain surgery after a triage nurse had categorized him in the highest level of emergency.

* * *

Okay, if this is real, where's Jesus? the old atheist's mind was still asking. *He must be here someplace. This is my chance to find out.*

"Jesus! *Je-sus!*" I began to call out as I looked around.

It wasn't that I refused to believe what was plainly before me. This was the afterlife, or some form of it, and I *knew* it.

"Jesus! *Jee-sus!*"

I couldn't find him.

At about the time this sneaky journalist was searching for Jesus, my physical body was in recovery from surgery.

The surgery, as described earlier, was performed by a giant-hearted Egyptian, Dr. Magdy Shady. I am grateful to Dr. Shady, not only for saving my life, but also because he, like most neurosurgeons, had had the foresight to find out what sort of work I performed for a living. He, therefore, exercised extraordinary care when dealing with the section of brain mass that oversees writing skills. It could not have been easy, either, because this is precisely where the peach-sized clot had continued to grow until his own expert excision.

Loved ones took turns in the recovery room, holding and patting my hand, murmuring loving, encouraging things that my subconscious mind might pick up. During my Jesus quest in the other world, Dad was taking his turn with me.

"Je-sus! Jesus!" I called out loud. "Jesus! *Jee-sus!*"

I was one mighty determined journalist. But think about it: what a scoop!

There is an old family story of a great-grandmother who, at her moment of death, claimed that Jesus was in the room, calling out to her. She in turn called out "Jesus!" a few times and then smiled, slumped back, and died.

"She's having visions!" kindly old, doddering, Monsignor Gustav Baer said to my Yankee grandma.

"Nurse, call my wife quick," Dad said when he heard me call that very name. "Tell her he's having visions!"

I still smile at that story, but there was nothing amusing about the moment of panic this gave my poor dad. If only he knew how happy I was and how wonderful it is to be in that place.

Jesus did not seem available to me, no matter how much I called. And I couldn't get into that beautiful, yellow-lit garden.

But I could get into one of the alcoves that lined the perimeter of this room. Within the alcoves, I knew innately, lay the connection between the physical and the metaphysical, and that once there, any of a number of options might occur.

One might be placed back into the physical world, for example. Or one might even be born anew, having the opportunity to "try again," that is, to relive one's entire life. One might be born again as the same soul but in a new body, thus supporting the "Bridey Murphy" crowd. One might even return in another life form, thus confirming the beliefs of so many millions of our Eastern brothers and sisters. One might also be permitted into that garden. Was it Paradise? Is Paradise the same thing as heaven? I never thought so, but I'm not so sure anymore.

But first a decision, or "judgment," was needed.

I was drawn into the inky depths of one of these alcoves, called by some unknown voice within me. Ever deeper I went until there, majestically before me in one breathless moment, was the Source of all light and good; of the motion of the planets and the music of the spheres; of all Love and of every good thing to which we humans aspire.

This was a transcendent moment of mystery and glory, hope and promise, and love—a love I had never known, a love so powerful that it would stay with me when brought back into the conscious world.

Upon returning, I remember being in a hospital bed, not knowing how I got back into this world. Mary Michael was at my bedside. Somehow I knew that I had had a stroke, no conversation was needed. Here before me was everything: my wife, my Mary Michael. And what's this? Not only was she here but she was covered—transcendently—by that same glorious yellow light seen through the windows of the "waiting room" I'd just left! It bathed her, enveloped her. And though the light shone *upon* her, instead of *within* as it had done with the shades, it had no visible source. I felt giddy, childlike, joyous! I felt filled to brimming with love, the same love that I had felt within that alcove and that had permeated the entire space in that way station, that world hovering between life and death.

The love stayed with me for a long, long time following this event—whenever, in fact, Mary Michael was with me.

Months later, when moved to question our gentle Irish priest, Father Murray, about these phenomena, I fully expected theological rebuttals and physical excuses involving drugs and comas and dreams. Instead, he asked a simple but profound question:

"Are you aware, Peter, that the Holy Spirit is the source of all love?"

* * *

I have described how, during the height of depression, the horrors of night often bring forth images of those who have caused real or imagined pain in one's past. Now I again called forth all the names and faces of those very same people, but this time my sense of unfinished business was different: I needed to forgive. This seemed like arrogance, but it was important—for my own sake—to reach down into the depths of my psyche to sweep out any remaining hints of anger or resentment against those who, within the scopes of their own jobs or their own lives, had caused real or imagined injury.

This little exercise came before the session with Father Murray. Afterward, I discovered that yet another person, completely neglected up to this point, was clearly the one most desperately in need of being freed of the very deepest resentments and hostilities:

I then forgave myself.

12

Tuscany Waits

> *February 2, 1993.* Home from Florida. No buyers for house, no good news from anywhere while I was gone. I'm getting into Mary Michael's habit of praying (yes, me!) for a miracle, which is what I was doing on my way to the mailbox this morning, hoping one of those damned sweepstakes she keeps entering would finally come through. Just where the path hooks a left, I remembered the voice I heard at that spot shortly after arriving home from Gaylord; the voice that told me to stop praying for things I can handle myself. In other words, don't look for miracle handouts, just write my damn story.

Okay, okay. It wasn't a voice in the physical sense. But the message, or impulse, was so strong and felt so much like an actual voice that I understood immediately what people like Billy Graham and Oral Roberts mean when they say that God "told" them to do this or that.

I also worried again, however briefly, about my own sanity, since this experience was undoubtedly close to what psychotics reportedly feel shortly before pressing the "up" button to the top of the University of Texas bell tower; or before setting things straight with the U.S. Postal Service by machine-gunning a dozen or so workers and patrons at the local branch; or before ordering their followers to drink cyanide-laced Kool-Aid.

Actually, I was no longer truly threatened by any real fear of insanity. Those days were long over, so from this time forward, I offered prayers for those who are caught, as I was at Gaylord, in that sticky black web of confusion that often accompanies brain injury.

I now knew what it was like to be honestly and truly crackers, and the living memory of it will stay with me throughout my days. I now also faced the single most difficult aspect of the entire brain-injury experience: being home.

Perhaps the most important aspect of recovery from a traumatic brain injury is the notion of getting back to work. This is especially difficult for people who work as freelancers. I had not had contract work since 1988, when I was an associate head writer on *Loving*. I had become resolved, however, since the TV writers strike, to set out in new directions. Shortly after the strike, my friend Dotson lectured me into the self-confidence I desperately needed, then set up a meeting for me with the editors of *Parade*, where he was a regular contributor. I soon became a regular contributor too.

Parade has as many quirks as any other magazine but the publication is basically quite good to its writers. When I asked for a raise in my fee, for example, it was tripled. Add to this the nature of the job, which is to travel virtually anywhere in the world, all expenses paid, to interview and report on the world's most interesting people, and there is virtually no cause for complaint, even when a job turns sour.

This happened only once in my experience, when I had gone deep into the jungles of Mexico to interview Lorraine Bracco, Sean Connery's co-star, you'll recall, in *Medicine Man.*

Medicine Man's production company had proven quite hostile, incomprehensible for a film in need of the major publicity afforded by *Parade*. For example, Matilda, the point woman, could make no promise of a car to meet me at the nearest airport in Veracruz, a difficult three-hour drive from the film company's camp in Catemaco, the Mexican backwater located near the jungle location set. I forged on from Mexico City not knowing what I would find.

At the Veracruz airport I spotted a driver bearing a sign that said "Medicine Man." Aha!

But the driver wasn't there for me. He was there to pick up Connery's stunt double, back from Mexico City after receiving a week's leave. They agreed to take me along.

The driver was an affable young Mexican named Herman (air-*monn*). The stunt double was a friendly Brit named Geoffrey (Jeff). Jeff proved to be an incurable Beatles fan, and Herman had chauffeured him many times previously, to judge by his fairly complete, if Spanish-accented, knowledge of "Can't Buy Me Love," "Till There Was You," and others. I jumped in for "Taxman," "Eleanor Rigby," and "We Can Work It Out," and all three of us were blasting full-tilt to the car stereo as we began down the driveway to the film camp. Suddenly, a *bandito* in a *bandillero* jumped into our headlights, brandishing a rifle and ordering us, in Spanish, to stop.

This proved to be the film company's private guard. Thank God for Herman, who was able to converse with him, providing certain passwords as he turned to assure us all was okay, explaining that this was merely an extra film company precaution after the entire payroll had been robbed by a full gang of *banditos* just the previous week.

When we arrived at the commissary, Matilda, my point

woman, was nowhere to be found. Herman unloaded my luggage and said he would find Matilda, so they would know what to do with me. Meanwhile, the commissary was open until 10:00 P.M. (it was 9:30), and so I was free to buy myself a beer or Pepsi while I waited. And waited.

An annoyed Matilda finally showed about two hours after the commissary closed. She said rather unpleasantly that I could stay here for tonight only, but then I would have to give up my room for the helicopter pilot who would be arriving to take Connery to the airport after the final day of his shooting.

Where would I stay once I gave up my room?

"The village is less than three miles away," Matilda said. "Maybe you'll find a hotel." Since there were no public phones on the grounds, could I use the company phones?

"There's a telephone in the village," Matilda told me.

Something was rotten in Catemaco.

But for tonight, anyway, I had a room.

What a room!

The "location camp" was actually a 1950s Mexican vacation motel, located on a lake just outside the village of Catemaco. It, like Catemaco, had seen better days.

The room I was given was scarred and beaten, filled with furniture that might have once been suitable for the Broadway Central Hotel long before it collapsed atop my first play. Empty beer bottles and soda cans were all over the ring-scarred dressers and tabletops. One of the drawers contained a two-month-old *Los Angeles Times*. There was a tiny bath with a shower that clanked only cold water and a sink that had more cigarette scars than my old buddy Mike's favorite ashtray. The place was filthy and the sheets were so soft and grimy that I, hardly a fussbudget, slept with my clothes on. Geckos, a small species of tropical lizard, scattered over the walls and ceilings all night long, letting out piercing little shrieks just loud enough to wake me up again and again after having grown accustomed to the clattering of an air conditioner that seemed to spew out only dying breaths.

Worst of all, I was informed the next morning that the director had now declared a "closed set." This meant I would not be permitted on the actual location grounds to interview Bracco.

That did it.

I told Matilda to inform the director there could be no interview under the circumstances. Calling collect, I left a message with my editor in New York and began packing.

Unfortunately (or fortunately, perhaps?) I had been denied further use of the camp's telephones and so, except by foot, there was no way out.

I was actually considering the foot option when there was a knock at my door. It was Matilda.

She had checked with the director, and it would now be okay for me to interview Bracco on the set, but not for three more days.

So there were now three days to fill in this strange, hot, dirty little place. What would I do?

I remembered a note I had received some time earlier from my play agent, Lois Berman. The note accompanied a check for, let's see, I think it was $1.75. It represented my share of the profits from the single copy of *The Interview* that had been sold during the previous three months. Clearly, after eighteen years, interest in *The Interview* had pretty much come to a standstill. I could hear what must have been Lois's sigh of exasperation as she wrote:

"Dear Peter . . . Are you *ever* going to write another play?"

I also remembered what had been my own determination during those years of television writing, especially for the soaps: I would find a way to get back to my true life's work, dammit, I *would!*

In fact, whenever people asked what I did for a living back then I would say, first, that I was a playwright. Then I would tell them that to support this habit I also wrote for television. But I never did have time to write plays.

Now, suddenly, I had time. Three whole days!

This dingy, revolting little 1950s Mexican motel on the lake, where I was now allowed to spend three more nights, no longer seemed quite so dingy and revolting.

I took my pens and legal pads down to the cracked, corroded swimming pool located on a bluff overlooking the lake. The scenery was beautiful. So beautiful and peaceful that, within my allotted three days, I sketched out a complete, three-act play, keeping in mind Eli Wallach, who'd been asking me for material. All I needed now was to actually write the play, *Moon and His Planets*, when I got home.

Beautiful, beautiful Catemaco!

Bracco turned out to be fun to interview. She also invited me to a party she was throwing for Sean Connery that night, in honor of his last day on the shoot. That meeting led to the interview I described earlier in this book.

On the following day I realized that my own mistreatment had been the result of some hot-headed dispute between Bracco and the director, John McTiernan. One way to strike back at a leading lady, one may surmise, is to make a major career-building (and ego-building) interview as difficult as possible to pull off.

But I pulled it off. I emerged unscathed, proud of myself, feeling I had earned some battle scars and a story to tell.

And a play, to boot!

I *loved* working for *Parade!*

But nowadays I had enough trouble walking to the mailbox and back. Jaunting all over the world was out of the question. There was also the problem of benefits and health coverage: Freelance journalists receive neither. I had taken out a low-cost policy through the Writers Guild, but this did not cover the bills of Gaylord. Some $30,000 remained unpaid, and we would have to come up with the balance, paying it off at an agreed-upon rate that would take us to the end of our lives.

Our Westhampton house had been on the market for years. We were still in the Reagan recession, and the house was being offered at an $80,000 loss, but people just weren't spending on luxury weekend homes. However, I had been inspired by my "voices" to write about my experiences so, hey, no problem.

The earliest notion of writing about my recovery didn't actually occur along the path to the mailbox. One of my very first impulses upon coming out of that coma a year earlier had been that you can't have a stroke at age forty-nine without at least finding a good story in it, not if you're a writer. This was during my initial hospitalization, when Mary Michael first brought me that pencil and pad for notes.

When I tell my story to others, they react by telling me that they admire my bravery. But is not *my* bravery that is to be admired. After all, what happened to *me?*

I experienced a brain hemorrhage in which there was no pain, no real discomfort beyond a little anxiety (all right, a *lot* of anxiety).

I promptly fell into a lengthy coma as dozens of accomplished pros whirred about, rushing me to the hospital, performing brain surgery, and so on.

I slept.

When I awoke, it was to the great confusion I have tried to describe in this book, and there were certainly some frightening times. But I was okay, really. I received three square meals a day, was given a rigorous routine of exercise and therapy, had all bases touched, all needs met. No, it wasn't I who suffered at all.

It was Mary Michael.

Left not only with the problem of figuring out how to deal with this unexpected stroke of fate but with the mess I'd left behind after two years of clinical depression, Mary Michael also had to deal with astronomical medical bills; faulty insurance coverage; an infuriatingly destructive IRS audit; the usual house, grounds, and pool maintenance; and the many problems, deadlines, applications, medical forms, and financial aid forms associated with two kids bound for college. And apart from the intervention of dependable friends, she had to do this solo. All in addition to running an interior design firm in which she is forced to smile while becoming deeply concerned with the problems of clients.

Somehow Mary Michael managed all this with good spirit, convincing herself that each person can do neither more nor less than to work through a given day at his or her own level of capacity. But as I've told you, Mary Michael is not merely wonderful. She is also funny. Many times it is her sense of dangerous, near-the-edge black comedy, often surpassing my own, that gets me through a rough period.

The night of the graduation party was my first time in bed with my wife in some three months. When I threw my deadweight left arm around her, it went into a wild tremor; a harmless, regular occurrence for those recovering from traumatic brain injury. It shook her—and the bed—at about a six on the Richter.

"My God, Peter," she said when the tremor eased, "this is like living under the El!"

On the following morning, during an amorous embrace in which she made a sudden turn that threw me from the bed and onto the floor, we both turned giddy and I made a lame remark about her failure to signal before turning.

"Didn't you see my bumper sticker?" she shot back. "Warning: I brake for TBIs."

One of the few searingly painful moments of these TBI years came upon recalling that our twenty-fifth wedding anniversary was approaching and that we would not be able to take Mary Michael's longed-for trip to Tuscany, about which she had dreamed and spoken often. We could not accomplish such a trip earlier when I worked in television because, while I earned more than enough, there was no time off. Now the situation was reversed, although I was as determined to somehow rent a small villa for a month or so in this most picturesque area of Italy as a special gift for her putting up with me as I had been to start walking or to begin writing again.

My version of the Tuscan dream, straight from *Architectural Digest*, involved a sepia-tinted villa surrounded by lush gardens filled with crumbling stone columns, sinewy marble statuary and dozens of tall, pointed cedars. Our nostrils would be filled with the earthy scents of fresh-baked bread, ripening grapes, and the nearby sea. Since our trip would be an excuse for others to visit Europe, friends and laughter would always be with us.

At some early point during our crisis, it had obviously occurred to Mary Michael that such a trip could not take place. Certainly not for our twenty-fifth. At the same time, she knew that there were several, possibly many, years of difficulty awaiting. To help give me courage, to help give me the hope and drive needed to succeed in the long, difficult, and painful period that lay ahead, she decided to provide a message of encouragement.

I can still recall when, finally off the respirator but exhausted after brain surgery, a rabid case of pneumonia, and that fifteen-day coma, I began to make out the hazy outline of something that had been placed at my feet. Eventually, I realized it was a sign, and then slowly, slowly made out its lettering. This is what it said:

Tuscany Waits

* * *

After a year of intensive, full-day therapy, it was time for a follow-up with my brain surgeon at Stony Brook University Hospital, Dr. Magdy Shady. While in the neurology section, I looked in on what had been my room during the days that immediately followed my stroke and tried to relive those moments of rediscovering the spiritual self I had lost for thirty-one years. This had been the most powerful and important moment of my life, and I wanted to see whether experiencing that same space might bring back some remnant of feeling, circumstance, or memory that would tell me it had just been part of some early delusion.

I was my own devil's advocate.

Nothing was found to change my mind, however, and every one of those memories remains as real and fresh as my children's births or my own wedding day.

One new memory I did recover upon returning to this space, though, is the one I have just reported: that of slowly awakening to the lovingly crafted sign that Mary Michael had placed at my feet, which could still be seen through my mind's eye as I looked into the vacant room that had been mine a year earlier.

This moment still inspires me during all-too-frequent moments of frustration.

"If she did what she had to do," I say to myself when my own going seems tough, "I sure as hell can do what I have to." When even thoughts of my young friends at Gaylord, Tom Cruise and Trevor Howard, can't wipe out my frustration, there is a fail-safe: two words that never, ever fail, which even now are taped to my computer screen:

Tuscany Waits

* * *

July 30, 1993. Mary Michael couldn't afford the time off, so Mom and Dad drove me up to the opening ceremonies of Gaylord's new natatorium, which is the one and only way Father Jim referred to the indoor pool facility that was under construction while we were there. Fantastic facility, but the day was a disappointment since no one showed.

I had been anxious to see Carolyn, the charming and thoughtful occupational therapist who had felt more pain than I with each creak and groan of a recalcitrant left shoulder, arm, and hand; and Jack, the social therapist who'd decided against turning me in to the Feds when I broke out of line during that emergency drill; and Susan, subject of Father Jim's soaring but off-key "If You Knew Susie"; and Jane, the cognitive therapist who'd insisted I learn to think and write again; and the many other members of the top-notch staff at this top-notch rehab hospital that my not-so-top-notch insurance company refused to cover.

I was even more keen to see my fellow alumni, to judge for myself how they'd fared back in real life: Ernie, with his Peter Pan Complex and his love of treats and goodies; Father Jim, the grammarian; Gertrude, Mother of All Mothers; Our Boy Hadjo, the Boy with a Head the Size of Cambodia; Gina, the Girl Who Does the Hemorrhagic Hop; my young pals, Tom Cruise and Trevor Howard; and Eddie, the Fireman Who Barks Like a Dog. Hell, I even wanted to see Willie the Whiner.

Above all others, though, I was anxious to see Charlie the Baker, who'd welcomed me to join him in the bliss and perfection of his Valley of the Snow Leopard. Had he, had anyone, found anything like the peace and joy I'd discovered (despite searing moments of readjustment turmoil) in returning to my Emily Kate, my Matt, my darling Mary Michael?

I was to be disappointed.

My thinking and perception skills were still—as they remain, albeit with steady improvement—pretty messed up. I had misread the invitation and shown up, instead, for a separate, more modest celebration involving only those who'd taken hydrotherapy. This had been elective and the only others I knew who'd opted for it were Tom Cruise and Trevor Howard, and they didn't show.

Not a word of complaint from Mom and Dad. This had been their treat, and they were going to make the most of it.

We took a walk around the beautiful grounds where Dad had pushed my chair so often. As we walked, I indulged in what would be perhaps my final "strolling" fantasy. I did this, I'm sure, because none of my old pals were actually there.

We went past the outdoor basketball court, where my mind's eye produced a light haze.

Here was Ernie, dribbling like a madman. He carefully launched his shot, which made its usual flawless arc, but circled ambivalently and dramatically around the rim, and then . . . and then . . . and then (I held my breath until) . . . in!

"*Yess!*" hissed Ernie, who turned to us with a wink as his sexy young wife suddenly appeared, embracing him at the foul line.

"I really *love* this game!" he said.

Behind him suddenly appeared Gina, the young Italian of the Hemorrhagic Hop and foul mouth. She took a shot and missed.

"Oh, fudge," she exclaimed.

Behind her appeared Jim, the Methodist minister whom Ernie had never failed to call "Father," a fact that had actually displeased the older man, though he never let on.

"Your shot, Reverend," Ernie said.

The minister smiled gratefully, then carefully eyed his shot, let fly and . . . missed.

He was happy, though, and with darned good reason. He'd been monitoring CNN for the two months he'd been home.

"And not a single dangling participle!" he exulted. "No split infinitives, no incorrect double negatives, and not a mixed metaphor in sight!"

All in all, I had a pretty good idea of what Father Jim's version of heaven was.

Tom and Trevor were suddenly there, too, chatting happily and meaningfully with their girlfriends about plans for graduate school after going on a lecture tour to spread awareness of brain damage. They were both considering acting careers.

A thicker fog arose, swirling and billowing in my own little "Field of Dreams" as the rest of my cast of characters slowly materialized: Carolyn and Susan and Judy and Jane and Jack and Hadjo and Willie; June Ann of the gnarled, twisted hands, and Georgette the little Austrian laser beam, and even Jacqueline, the corpulent teenager who had cried great gooey gobs when she couldn't withdraw her life savings from the Easy Street Savings and Loan in order to reach her sweet old granny in Elmira, New York.

Everyone I'd known at this happily unforgettable healing place was suddenly assembled in fancy, if not reality.

Suddenly, from across the expanse of carefully manicured lawn we all—except for Mom and Dad, of course—heard a middle-aged woman happily summoning everyone to Sunday dinner in the beautiful, large log cabin on these bucolic hospital grounds.

"Din-ner! *Dinn-err!*" she called cheerfully.

Who else but Gertrude, Mother of All Mothers?

She had baked an enormous stuffed turkey, had glazed a

ham or two, and had made enough gravy and biscuits, creamed spinach, yams, apple pie, and pineapple upside-down cake for all of us.

But wait. There, on the huge porch of the log cabin . . . was that . . . could it be . . . Charlie?

Yes, there was good old Charlie, beaming as he stood surrounded by wife, sons, daughters-in-law, and grandchildren, hugging them, laughing at the kids, having the time of his life.

"See this, Peter?" he said, opening his arms wide to his family and using my correct name for the first time.

"Was I right, or what?"

I had to agree.

The snow leopard had led him to just the right spot.

* * *

As for me, I had become unemployable, as I was still, in fact, incapable of functioning on all cylinders. Our house was still on the market; we had endured a heartless and harrowing IRS audit; a tax lien was placed on our house, should it *ever* sell; our kids were both headed for college; and we were borrowing to survive.

Even with the ability to laugh at myself, it became increasingly difficult to avoid slipping into depression once again.

This became a more distinct threat with the arrival of spring and with it the twentieth—*twentieth*—anniversary of the collapse of the Mercer Arts Center.

I had to ask: What happened to the promise? What happened to my wife's dreams, my family's future? What happened to "Remember the name: Peter Swet"?

Had it all been buried twenty years ago, truly lost forever in the debris of a long-forgotten theatre?

Finally, finally, after weeks of steeling myself, after learning to accept that I would simply have to start my writing career all over again in some new way, I came up with the one and only answer I could possibly live with:

"Hell, no."

And then I flipped my computer's "on" switch.

Epilogue

Hey, Maybe You Really Can Go Home Again

Yes, there have been losses. And certainly there have been many changes since that day five years ago when I resolved to help save our house and my family's future by resuming my writing career. But I resolved that this writing—my story—would not merely place my name out there once again as a viable writer. It would also help countless others to understand the world of the brain injured. And shared experiences from the spiritual realm would, without seeming overtly evangelical, reassure at least some doubters that there is, indeed, a warmth and a welcome in God's love. Now, how can you turn away from that?

But back in the practical world of the Swet family, there was just no selling our House of the Spitting Turtle. We lost it.

Well, okay, "lost" is a bit melodramatic. The truth is, we were forced to sell at an outlandishly low price because of a pile of debt and because the insurance policy I had chosen through the Writers Guild of America wouldn't cover Gaylord's room and board on the grounds that I didn't need to be hospitalized for rehabilitation. (After being unable to work due to depression, I couldn't afford the more expensive policy that had been available.)

The insurance company's case is that while it covered needed therapies following brain trauma, I could have and should have stayed at home. I didn't require hospitalization, you see, throughout those months when I thought someone was trying to rip my liver out and I was otherwise near-maniacal. My wife and kids should have handled me. Their problem. Not the insurance company's.

Gaylord was quite gracious and cooperative, though, placing us on a long-term payment plan. But because of this and other debt, we quite literally left the house closing unable to take ourselves to dinner in celebration of being rid not so much of the House of the Spitting Turtle, but of the extraordinary debt it represented. The "up" side was that thousands no longer had to be borrowed each month to meet the ridiculous mortgage taken on during my yuppie years, a time of which I am not proud. We were free!

Free, yes, but broke. And with no place to live.

Thanks to quick action by more of those first-rate Westhampton friends, we soon found ourselves in a quite manageable rental on a beautiful saltwater creek where our back view encompassed nesting swans, egrets, great herons, and all manner of large wading birds as well as an occasional herd of foraging deer. We had no cause to complain.

We were fortunate, indeed.

June 18, 1996. Life seems close to what I remember as normal. Emotions are less skewed, and I cry or fall into senseless laughter less often. But I do become inappropriately angry at times. I am always ticked, for example, at not being permitted to drive, though I know it's because of the seizures that are a legacy of brain surgery. There are enough idiots behind the wheel these days without adding a few hundred thousand more with violently seizing brains.

A brain seizure is not pleasant. A minor one usually involves just passing out cold, but the major one? Not very pretty. As if stricken with epilepsy, I would fall to the ground, moaning and shouting, usually without my own knowledge. My left arm and leg—and only the left—would flail wildly about, under the control of some offstage Geppeto. My mouth would foam (I still don't understand why). Most embarrassing, I would pee in my pants. And not just some little amount.

Soon consciousness would return, and with it the need for plenty of rest and sleep for the next couple of days.

Before this was all brought under control with medication, an attack was my greatest fear. But here again, Mary Michael found a way to help me through the fear. On my first solo trip, by train, to Manhattan for a visit with an old college friend, Jim Thesing, I found a message waiting for me on his answering machine when we got to his Riverside Drive apartment:

"Hi, Jim. Hi, Peter. It's Mary Michael. Peter, don't forget to take your meds on schedule. Remember, you're in Manhattan now: If you have a seizure, people will simply think you're break dancing." Mary Michael was again forcing me to face my demons with laughter.

But while it's important to find the humor that is so often before you, please don't think this long recovery has been a barrel of yuks, easily handled by two glib forty-to-fifty-somethings left over from the 1970s *Saturday Night Live* crowd. Oh, no. We certainly do have our difficult times, fights included. And we do feel consumed by our losses, dog-tired from the daily struggle to find yet another technique for getting through yet another stress-filled day in which we no longer own our own house or get out to dinner or get a vacation or a break in any other way than with *Seinfeld* or *Frasier.*

The stress certainly makes us wonder at times, sometimes loudly, what we are doing in this relationship and with our lives. But even in the height of anger, when one feels ready to quit (and many in this situation do quit), we have something else going for us, something quite beyond love: commitment. Commitment to a promise made long ago and commitment to our kids, two young people whom we placed in this world and who are just starting out in it. But mostly, I know, it is commitment to a promise that endures for richer or poorer, in sickness and health, that was made over twenty-five years ago at St. Veronica's on East 79th Street in Manhattan by two twenty-somethings who, while on their way to buildings that crash and minds that blow and brains that damage, were also on their way to a rather grand party at Tavern on the Green, a party that in many ways just isn't over.

* * *

> *June 20, 1996.* It occurred to me that in visiting my sister in the past, I'd rarely ever left her apartment and had therefore not seen the old neighborhood since I left for Manhattan in 1964, at age twenty-one. Today I changed that.

My first stop was at 88th Street, where I'd spent most of my years growing up. There, before house number 95-10, was the spot where a tree once stood, a spot at which Dad took super 8 movies of all the neighborhood kids each year in their Easter finery (I can still see that same endless progression of one child after another awaiting Dad's off-camera signal and then, with Easter baskets in hand and goofy, uneasy smiles on well-scrubbed faces, walking stiffly and uneasily toward Dad's lens and immortality).

But my sister, Patricia, and her little Patricia, her little Anthony, and her little Debra were no longer there. In place of them and in place of Elsie and Kayo, and Mrs. Ozga and Mrs. Marak and the Santoros and Vito and Josie and my old man's buddy Reno, with his wife, Annie, and their little ones, there were now—strangers!

That spot had seen many ring-o-leevio games and red-light green-light games and giant steps games and Johnny-on-the-pony games with the Houser kids and the Spencer kids and my cousins, the Jakubowski kids. That was the very spot at which I'd once waited patiently for the Bungalow Bar truck with cousins Billy and Stanley and Carol; where we all once feasted on Ring-dings and Yankee Doodles and Dreamsicles and Mister Goodbars; where the hotdog man regularly served up two for a quarter and where we caught lightning bugs at dark. Yes, there on that hallowed ground of childhood now stood—strangers!

And the strangers were no longer Polish and Italian and German, as they had been. They were new immigrants. And instead of the simple babble of Brooklynese there now seemed the babble of, well, Babel, in an area no longer the Ozone Park of my childhood.

I walked past my old school and the parish church, St. Elizabeth's, which had governed it. I walked past the houses and apartments once known so intimately; there now seemed so many more dreary two-, three-, and four-family wood frame houses refaced with "contemporary" 1950s "fieldstone" (which was anything but) on the bottom half, and ubiquitous green or gray asbestos siding on top. Nearly every facade had been "modernized" with a fifties picture window that no longer looked out onto a vaguely picturesque street peopled with harmless, useful umbrella men and banana men and knife sharpeners and ragpickers, but onto streets now alive with junkies, hoods, and "chop shop" hustlers, many of them hurling verbal abuse at spouses, children, and neighbors in some unknown tongue. It was a hostile world.

And so much grubbier than I'd ever dreamed possible.

Finally, I reached the old convent with its memories of Sister Attila Marie and her tribe of cohorts. Then I entered—bravely, perhaps—St. Elizabeth's church.

I say bravely because I had expected unrecognizable change, perhaps even graffiti, but the old place was in good—even terrific—shape, and seemed exactly as it had in my earliest childhood.

The scent of long-burned incense still hung heavy, and a light haze filled the space, punctuated by vivid little slants of color shafting down from the assortment of brightly stained glass saints who had not changed positions or attitude since those days when it had been my job to escort my old Yankee grandma to 8:00 Mass every morning.

The memory held such power that I could very nearly hear the heaving and belching of Mrs. Francie Roggeman's organ and could easily visualize her tiny figure, black hat with feathers and veil all askew, sitting at the organ console in the choir loft, about to be gobbled by the huge array of pipes pushing in on all sides as she swayed undeterred to some decidedly catchy rhythm unavailable to the rest of us in the Bach and Handel, the Purcell and Verdi and Wagner she so faithfully wheezed out every day.

But this was not the only memory to be found inside the church of childhood. If I squinted my eyes I could see, kneeling way back in that very last row, beneath the loft and not far from

Father Lineback's old confessional—Yes! My old Yankee grandma. I went to her. Wasn't it my job to walk her home?

She took me by the arm and pulled hard as, with Mass having ended and Francie Roggeman exiting the congregation with a little something from "Tannheiser," I escorted her down the steps and outside.

Past the school we went. Past the flagpole and the large, cement-covered schoolyard where all of us schoolchildren would assemble for morning Rosary, the Pledge of Allegiance, and, as we all gazed out onto the filth and soot of busy Atlantic Avenue, a quick verse or two of "America the Beautiful."

Past all the old neighbors' multi-family homes and the occasional, but rare, private house we went. Past the Sikorskis. Past the homes of schoolmates Colin Bolger and Marianne Beisel and Billy Roller and Angelina Amorino. Past "the flats," an ominous-looking tenement where a woman called Aunt Angie had once maintained an excessively decorated private altar, which she considered so remarkable that she kept it open at regular hours for people of the neighborhood to visit. Even more remarkable was that so many people of the neighborhood actually came to see this, to kneel, to pray, perhaps to expect a crying Madonna or two.

Finally, we reached the two-family house where we lived when I was quite young and we were quite poor, before moving on to the magnificence of 95-10 88th Street, already described.

Suddenly, Grandma disappeared back into my memory files and, instead, I could once again see Uncle Joe at the door saying, "Well, if it ain't Pete and Re-Pete. Where you boys goin'?"

"I'm gonna play baseball, Uncle Joe," I faithfully say.

"You're learnin' from the best," he repeats for the hundred thousandth time.

"I know that, Uncle Joe" is my hundred thousandth response.

Then Uncle Joe disappears again.

And, in real time again, I knew what I must do.

I walked onward to the 88th Street Park, past Old Man Dana's vegetable stand and Al & Adelaide's candy store and all the old routes of the umbrella man and the rag man and the banana man. I walked past Mr. Peretta's barbershop, which, having gone through many metamorphoses since those days of the late forties and early fifties, is now as shuttered and dark as Al & Adelaide's and Old Man Dana's and Otto & Tina's and every other former shop along this once-bustling strip of Atlantic Avenue. Now, every last storefront was covered with those ubiquitous pull-down security grates, giving the old neighborhood strip the appearance of a gulag in 1950s Siberia. All that was missing was barbed wire fencing and the occasional guard tower with dogs and machine guns.

And there, finally before me, lay my goal: the 88th Street Park. I walked slowly along its border, peering through the tall chain-link fence at the old handball courts and basketball courts and on to my ultimate goal, the old softball field. To my surprise, all of these old facilities were still here although nothing was in use. Now, not a soul played in this once-jammed complex of urban pastimes. I walked the long way across 88th Street from the old softball field, recalling how, as a child, I would often take a circuitous route to avoid this very spot for fear that some kids playing ball in the park would hit one over the fence and the others would all yell "Hey, kid—get the ball!"

Me? Get a ball? Show the world I threw like a girl? No way! Better to walk around the next block. I would have walked miles to avoid facing that.

Even now, a blush came to this fifty-year-old face in recollection of the horror and shame once felt by that four-year-old in the park. Would I carry my shame always?

But wait! There, across the street and through the fence, was *the* spot, that very spot. If I went across and through the playing field, would I still find the figures of Vito and Reno standing there? Of Cheech? Of Kayo, Matches, Sonny Munch, and Eddie Arturo, all surrounding that little boy who couldn't even throw a ball to his softball champion dad? I would find out.

Into the park I went, toward that group of men surrounding the little boy. I strode directly up to where the group had stood, in the shade of a tree that had by now quadrupled in size. But when I got to the spot—*the* spot—what do you know? Empty! No one and nothing there. No desperate feelings of shame. No anger, no hurt—all of it, vanished. Safely consigned to memory along with Grandma and Uncle Joe and Aunt Anna's bastafazool.

I had faced my ghosts. Now they were gone.

* * *

Dad died suddenly on October 17, 1996, surprise victim of congestive heart failure. We all miss him terribly, most especially Mom, who had loved him deeply and tenderly since they'd run off to elope in Gaithersburg, Maryland, as fourteen- and fifteen-year-olds some sixty years earlier. My own grief, while also deep, is mixed with the satisfaction of having gotten to know him and with a sincere gratitude for all that has happened, including the horrifying illness that brought such extraordinary gifts.

I continue to show modest physical improvements and am happily back at my writing despite the mental confusion, the memory difficulties, and sheer addle-mindedness that can make it quite infuriating. I can't complain, of course, and don't. Yet I sometimes wonder whether I would choose to go through the experience, all of it, again. The answer must be no, because it has brought my family far too much stress, pain, and difficulty.

But if there were only myself to consider? You bet I'd do it again. No problem. Because despite having lost everything that seems worthwhile to most Americans: house, bank account, investments, job and career, I have gained so very much: peace with my own neurosis; an easy forgiveness of both Dad and myself; an understanding of just how good people can be; the very important and very happy rediscovery of God and His all-pervasive love. And with it all comes something else that is terribly, terribly important—something very few people are ever offered in life and of which I must now take full advantage:

A second chance.

ABOUT THE AUTHOR

After growing up in Queens, New York, PETER SWET became an award-winning television writer, journalist, and playwright whose works have been seen and performed throughout the United States, Canada, Europe, and Australia, and performed by some of the most well-known names in entertainment. He currently resides with his wife, Mary Michael Rinaldi, in Riverside, Connecticut.

HAZELDEN PUBLISHING AND EDUCATION is a division of the Hazelden Foundation, a not-for-profit organization. Since 1949, Hazelden has been a leader in promoting the dignity and treatment of people afflicted with the disease of chemical dependency.

The mission of the foundation is to improve the quality of life for individuals, families, and communities by providing a national continuum of information, education, and recovery services that are widely accessible; to advance the field through research and training; and to improve our quality and effectiveness through continuous improvement and innovation.

Stemming from that, the mission of the publishing division is to provide quality information and support to people wherever they may be in their personal journey—from education and early intervention, through treatment and recovery, to personal and spiritual growth.

Although our treatment programs do not necessarily use everything Hazelden publishes, our bibliotherapeutic materials support our mission and the Twelve Step philosophy upon which it is based. We encourage your comments and feedback.

The headquarters of the Hazelden Foundation are in Center City, Minnesota. Additional treatment facilities are located in Chicago, Illinois; New York, New York; Plymouth, Minnesota; St. Paul, Minnesota; and West Palm Beach, Florida. At these sites, we provide a continuum of care for men and women of all ages. Our Plymouth facility is designed specifically for youth and families.

FOR MORE INFORMATION ON HAZELDEN, please call **1-800-257-7800**. Or you may access our World Wide Web site on the Internet at **http://www.hazelden.org**.